Contents

1 Safety in the Home

Home to most people is a place of refuge. Here they feel safe and secure. Most of us choose to disregard the dangers around us once we have entered our own front door. As a result more people die or are crippled from accidents in the home than those on the road. While there are no official records on home accidents it has been estimated that approximately three million people are treated in hospitals and thirty million by their own doctor for injuries incurred at home. Nearly 80% of accidents causing death happen to the most vulnerable age groups, people over sixty-five and children under five. More than one thousand children die each year as a result of accidents in the home and nearly 90% of these are under five years of age.

The main causes of injury are falls, poisoning, burns, scalds, suffocation and choking. Even trivial accidents can cause much suffering and worry for the victim and the family.

Whilst the majority of home accidents occur in the kitchen, the living room, and on the stairs, many of the causes are common to every part of the house.

Living Today **Book 2**

Health and Care of the Family

In the same series

Good Grooming and Clothes Care
Feeding the Family
Housing the Family
Decorating Your Home
Homemaking

Living Today Book 2

Health and Care of the Family

Margaret Cullen

Illustrated by John Plumb

Heinemann Educational Books. London

Heinemann Educational Books Ltd
LONDON EDINBURGH MELBOURNE AUCKLAND TORONTO
SINGAPORE HONG KONG KUALA LUMPUR IBADAN
NAIROBI JOHANNESBURG NEW DELHI

ISBN 0 435 42201 4

First Published 1971

Reprinted 1973

Designed by Design Practitioners Limited, Sevenoaks

Published by Heinemann Educational Books Ltd
48 Charles Street, London W1X 8AH

Printed in Great Britain by Butler & Tanner Ltd
Frome and London

1 Good lighting is essential in all parts of the house. Switches should be easily reached on entering every room and passage so that there is no need to go anywhere in the house in the dark. This includes attics, cellars and the path to the coal shed or garage.

2 Floors should be kept in good repair. Floor coverings should be firmly fixed so that they cannot slide or curl up at the edges. They should be repaired or discarded before holes or frayed edges become a danger. Avoid using small rugs and slip mats.

3 Windows should be checked for safety. Grills or vertical bars should be fitted in all upstairs rooms used by children or where the sill is low enough to allow an adult to fall should he lose his balance. Make sure catches work easily without danger or damaging fingers. If the window 'sticks', be careful to avoid putting your hand through the glass when trying to force it open. Put a piece of wood across the window from one frame to another and bang gently on this rather than on the frame.

4 Doors should not open into areas of circulation or where there is likely to be a collision. Sliding doors are a good alternative and give the advantage of extra space. Take care where you use glass doors and make sure they are fitted with toughened glass. 'Stable' type doors are useful in preventing small children and animals from wandering.

5 Storage should be planned so that articles in frequent use are within easy reach. Should you need to get something that is out of reach you should use a step ladder. Do not try to balance on a stool or on boxes as these could easily slip. Get help when you need to push or carry more weight than you can carry on your own or anything which prevents you seeing where you are going.

6 All dangerous drugs, medicines and poisonous household substances should be locked up or stored where it would be impossible for a child to reach them. This precaution applies to potentially dangerous things such as matches, razor blades, knives, scissors and needles. Babies can often climb even before they have learned to walk and invariably try to get hold of the very things you are trying to keep from them.

7 Overfurnished and cluttered rooms are dangerous. Try to keep your home tidy with a safe place planned for everything.

8 Broken furniture should be repaired straight away or put away until this can be done. Get rid of such things as disused refrigerators or trunks which are big enough for a child to get into, but difficult for him to get out of again. There have been many tragic cases of small children being trapped and suffocated while using these as hiding places. If they must be kept, lock up securely and remove the key or dismantle the door or lid completely.

9 Buy for safety. Look out for the safety symbols which

guarantee that the article concerned has been thoroughly tested and passed as safe.

10 Read manufacturers instructions and follow them when using the article. Make sure all equipment is installed and serviced by experts.

11 Have all gas and electrical systems checked regularly.

12 Remember to guard all fires. You are legally obliged to do this to fires in all rooms used by children under twelve years of age.

13 Make sure no appliance with open flame or radiant burners are placed where curtains can blow on to them and catch fire. If necessary consider replacing curtains with venetian or roller blinds.

14 Little girls and elderly ladies are safer in pyjamas than in flowing nightdresses. Buy or make these in fabrics which have been chemically fire-proofed such as Proban. Wash according to instructions so that you do not remove the chemicals.

15 Do not hang mirrors above fireplaces.

Fire Prevention

1 Pay heed to the correct use of gas, electricity and oil.

2 Guard all fires.

3 Never carry burning coal from one fire in order to start another.

4 Take care where you leave hot ashes. Use a metal container with a tight lid.

5 Never use petrol or paraffin to start a fire or to boost it when it is dying down.

6 Do not use a piece of paper across a fireplace to help draw up a fire. The paper can very easily catch fire and cause a fire outside the fireplace.

7 Do not dispose of oily or greasy paper or cloths in the fireplace. These can flare out into the room or set the chimney on fire.

8 Chimneys should be swept regularly.

9 All flammable liquids such as petrol, paraffin and cleaning fluids should be kept in a cool place away from the house and from any source of heat. They should be in metal containers in a brick or stone building or even buried in a marked place in the ground. Never store more than is absolutely necessary.

10 Children love to play with matches and lighters. These should be kept out of their reach. Older children should be shown how to light matches correctly. It should be stressed that this is not a game, and should be done only when necessary, and under strict supervision of an adult.

11 Cigarete ends should be put into ashtrays designed so that the stubs cannot fall or be blown out of the tray.

12 Be very careful when using aerosols. Many contain flammable liquids and should not be used in a closed area where there is a naked flame. Use according to the makers instructions. Store in a cool place and put them in the dustbin when emptied. Never pierce them or put them on a fire as you may cause an explosion.

What to do if fire is discovered

1 Don't panic.
2 Get everyone out of the room where the fire is. If someone's clothes catch fire he should be rolled on the floor to smother the flames. If possible roll him in a blanket or rug but speed is the most important thing.
3 Close all doors and windows. This will help to isolate the fire which thrives on draughts.
4 Call the Fire Brigade.
5 Get everyone out of the building.
6 If you are cut off by the fire shut yourself in a room with a window. Block the gap under the door with cushions or rugs to stop smoke filtering. Only then should you open the window to shout to attract attention.
7 If you are alone in the house when a fire breaks out you may have to decide whether prompt action with a bucket of water or an extinguisher would put out the fire. If there is any doubt at all, play safe and call the Fire Brigade. They are the experts and their services are free.

Fire Extinguishers
These are not a substitute for the Fire Brigade, but all large fires start as small ones. The purpose of an extinguisher is to check the fire in its early stages. Care must be taken in choosing the correct type of extinguisher and making sure it is in good condition. The Fire Protection Association is always willing to give advice on the subject.

Types of Extinguisher
1 Pressurised water containers suitable for use on furniture and fittings as they cool the surface as well as putting out the flames. They should not be used for flammable liquids or electricity. The most useful size has the capacity of about 4 litres. A larger size than this might be too heavy for women or old people.
2 Dry powder extinguisher which blankets the flames. It should hold about 1 kilogramme.

3 CO_2 type which 'suffocates' the flames. The most effective size is about 2 kilogrammes. The dry powder and CO_2 type extinguishers can both be used for flammable liquids and for electrical fires.

The fire extinguisher designed for use on carburettor fires in small vehicles and boat engines should never be used in the home as they contain toxic agents.

The instructions for use should be printed on the appliance. These should be carefully studied. If it shows any sign of deterioration the appliance should be discarded immediately. For complete protection you should have several extinguishers placed at danger points around the house. The average house needs the water type in the hall and on the landing, and a powder or CO_2 type in the kitchen and garage.

If you cannot have any of these, you can protect your home fairly effectively by keeping a fire bucket full of sand in the kitchen, and garage, and a garden hose kept ready near a tap.

The Safe Use of Electricity

Electricity in the home has several great advantages from the safety point of view.

1 It heats without a naked flame.
2 It cuts itself off automatically by blowing a fuse if anything goes wrong.
3 The British Electrical Regulations and Codes of Practice are of a very high standard.
4 It can be used safely for lighting, heating, and water heating in every part of the house.
5 If you buy a new appliance carrying the seal of the British Electrical Approval Board you can be sure it has been rigorously tested and is safe to use.
6 The Electricity Board will advise you on the suitability and use of the appliance you buy.

However, this safety can be jeopardized if you are careless. Safety can only be assured if you are sensible in the use of electricity.

Precautions with electricity

1 Make sure all installations, repairs and extensions are carried out by a qualified electrician. This will ensure that all wiring is effectively insulated and earthed.

2 Have sufficient lighting sockets and power points for all the equipment you are likely to use.

3 Have frayed flexes, broken plugs and switches repaired immediately.

4 Do not have long flexes where people could trip over them. Never hide flex under floor coverings as wear could go undetected and cause a shock or start a fire.

5 Use the correct gauge fuse wire in fuse boxes and the correct rate cartridge fuse in appliances on ring circuits. If the flow of electricity exceeds the safety limit the fuse will blow and break the circuit. The supply of electricity is automatically cut off before damaging wiring or fittings. If the fuse blows more than twice consult an expert as this is a danger signal.

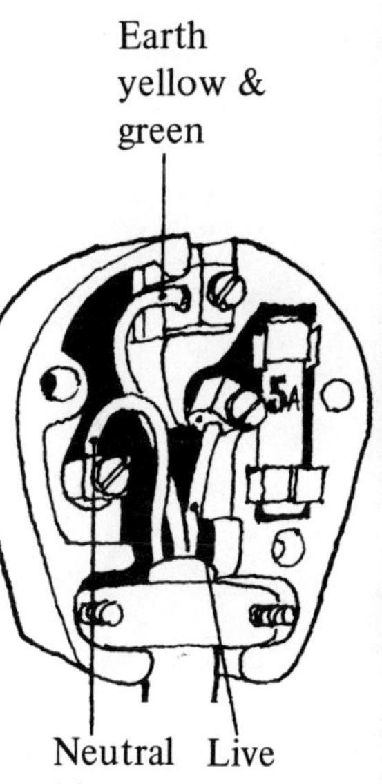

6 Use fused three pin plugs for all appliances, not two pin plugs. They may work so connected, but are not safe. If plugs or switches warm up in use have them serviced at once as they could prove dangerous.

7 Never take portable electrical appliances into the bathroom. Appliances for use in the bathroom should be fixtures with sockets outside the bathroom and switched on outside the room, or by pull cords inside.

8 Never switch on electrical appliances with wet hands.

9 Lamp sockets should be used for lamp bulbs only. Never use them for irons, fires, or cleaners.

10 Do not fill a kettle with water while it is still plugged in.

11 Switch off electricity at the main control before cleaning the cooker.

12 Do not leave an iron switched on and then leave it unattended.

13 It is sensible to remove plugs from sockets when appliances are not in use. Unplug them at night or if you are to be away during the day.

14 Store appliances in a cool dry place.

15 Turn off the electricity at the main whenever you are doing any minor repairs to the wiring, changing a fuse, or if the house is to be left unoccupied.

The safe use of gas in the home

Gas has the advantage of giving a speedy and variable heat or light. It can be supplied through the mains or in special containers which makes its use possible in boats and caravans as well as in country areas. It has a characteristic smell which gives warning of leakage. Gas is poisonous but is rendered safe by burning it in correct conditions. It must be burnt in a sufficient supply of air or it will exhaust the oxygen in the air and form carbon monoxide fumes. Carbon monoxide is a highly poisonous gas and as it has no smell or colour it gives no warning of its presence.

Gas can be used safely if you take these sensible precautions.

1 Make sure all gas installations, repairs and inspections are carried out by skilled workmen.

2 Buy gas equipment which has been tested and approved by the British Standards Institute. If in doubt ask your local Gas Board for advice.

3 Make sure all air vents and flues are kept clean and free from blockage.

4 Most gas appliances can be bought or fitted with safety taps. Bayonet fixing should be used when possible as this turns off the supply of gas should a fitting be disconnected.

5 Follow manufacturers' instructions for use of all apliances.

6 Do not bath while the gas geyser in the room is alight.
7 Turn off all gas taps before putting money into the gas meter.
8 Guard all fires.
9 Turn off supply at the mains when leaving the house for any length of time.
10 Never ignore the smell of gas. If there is the slightest suspicion of a leak turn off the gas at the main and open doors and windows. Inform the Gas Board immediately.
11 Do not investigate a gas leak with a naked flame.

Safe Use of Oil

Oil is an inexpensive fuel which can be bought in large or small quantities. It can be used for heating, cooking and lighting. The greatest number of accidents are caused by the incorrect use of heaters.

1 Oil is a highly flammable liquid. Care must be taken in transport and storage.
2 Use the correct grade of oil recommended by the maker of the equipment
3 Buy equipment which complies with British Standards Institutes Safety Regulations.
4 Avoid buying secondhand equipment. This may be dangerous.
5 Follow manufacturers' instructions for use of all appli- of equipment.
6 Never use equipment which is damaged in any way. Take it to a reputable dealer and have it properly repaired or replace it.
7 Keep wicks clean and trimmed according to instructions.
8 A heater should only be used on a level surface where it cannot be knocked over, preferably on a base which cannot burn, such as a metal tray.
9 Ideally a heater should be used in a fireplace. The opening

to the chimney should be screened to give twenty square inches of ventilation.

10 When possible the heater should be fixed so that it cannot be knocked over by the children or animals. All fires should be guarded.

11 Whilst the room should be well ventilated the heater should be kept out of draughts and away from any material which could blow on to it and burn, articles such as curtains or laundry being dried.

12 Do not allow children to touch the heater at any time, or to be left in the house alone with a lighted heater.

13 Never move the heater while it is alight.

Safety Symbols

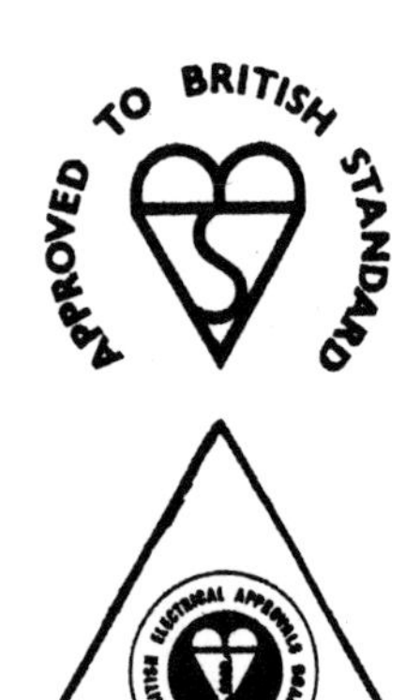

1 **The 'Kite' Mark.**
This is the mark of the British Standard Institute.

Look for this when buying fireguards, oil heaters, electric blankets, electric plugs and sockets, step ladders, flame resistant fabrics, pressure cookers, cots and many other articles.

2 **The BEAB Symbol.**
The mark of the British Electrical Approval Board. Look for it when buying any domestic electrical appliances.

3 **The OAMA Symbol.**
This seal of the Oil Appliance Manufacturers Association. It incorporates the mark of the British Standards Institute. Look for this sign when buying oil heating appliances.

4 **The Gas Council Symbol.**
All appliances sold in gas showrooms have to undergo severe tests before they are approved. All appliances and fittings must conform to the British Standards specification.

Safety in the Living Rooms

The living room of the house where the whole family meets, where friends are entertained, and a wide variety of activities are carried out should be the one where you are safest. In fact it is the room where you could be most at risk. Many of the hazards have already been mentioned but there are others which are more likely to be found here than elsewhere.
The family life is centred around the living room so you must be prepared to deal with the safety problems of the very young and the very old, the active members of the family and those who prefer sedentary occupations.

All the general rules for safety apply here. Flooring must be safe, fires must be guarded and gas and electrical appliances used intelligently. Be sparing with furniture polish. A shining floor looks attractive but if it should be the cause of someone slipping and hurting himself it is a luxury you should do without.

Toddlers will grab at anything available to help steady their faltering steps. They are also curious and will try to reach for things on the table or sideboard.

If the table is covered with a cloth or the sideboard with a runner overhanging the edge, it is only too easy for the child to grab it and pull down a teapot of scalding tea, or heavy ornaments onto himself. Use table mats when young children are around or fold the cloth to just fit the top of the table with no overhang.

It is obvious that small children will play on the floor and have a variety of toys to occupy them. Train them from an early age to collect up all their toys and put them away when they finish playing. While one is naturally alert for toys on the floor when children are present, it is easy to overlook and trip over them when the children have gone elsewhere.

As with a radio it is most unwise for an amateur to tamper with a television set. Leave repairs to the expert. Because of the high voltages involved they can be extremely dangerous. Make sure the set is disconnected from the electricity supply before any servicing is carried out. When you are not watching the television remember to switch off at the main switch as well as on the set.

Keep the amount of furniture to the minimum and avoid a clutter of ornaments or other unnecessary items. Train the family to keep these rooms tidy and to put away their own possessions when they have finished using them.

The Kitchen

The kitchen is the workshop of the home. It is also the main source of danger. The workshop in industry is regularly inspected to make sure every precaution is taken to protect the workers from harm. In the home an equally rigorous inspection should be undertaken by the homemaker.

Much of the equipment now available is a boon in lightening the work of the homemaker but it could be a source of danger if incorrectly installed, badly maintained or carelessly used.

Plan the kitchen to be as safe a place as possible, the cooker should not be next to doorways. Sliding doors are often safer than hinged doors, on cupboards as well as entrances.

There should be a flat surface next to the oven so that you have somewhere to put hot dishes as you take them out. The main storage should be between eye and knee level. This avoids unnecessary bending and stretching. The area below and above this should be used to store things seldom used. A step ladder should be used to reach high storage.

High level ovens with separate hobs are safer to use than the conventional stove and are not very much more expensive.

Plan storage for small equipment as carefully as for your large appliances. Kitchen and carving knives should be stored separately from the gadgets. Keep them well sharpened. A blunt knife is dangerous as it slips instead of cutting. Use a rotary tin opener rather than the old fashioned 'spike' type because these open tins cleanly without jagged edges.

Pay special attention to floors. The ideal covering has yet to be found but the nearest to this as yet is probably a good quality vinyl. This melts with dry heat but stands up well to water and grease. It is easy to cut and lay and inexpensive enough to allow for replacement when needed. Mop up water or grease as soon as it is spilled before anyone has the mischance to slip. Use cleaners recommended by the manufacturer, not polishes which give a slippery shine. Do not have loose rugs or mats in the kitchen other than a heavy one at the outer door.

Children (and animals) should be kept out of the kitchen unless they are safely in a playpen. They can easily hurt themselves, or cause injury to others, by getting in the way, or leaving toys on the floor to be tripped over.

We take it for granted that a car needs to be regularly serviced and checked for safety. The equipment in the kitchen is often worked harder than our cars but is often allowed to go unchecked until it breaks down.

Take all precautions necessary when using electricity. Take no chances. Electricity plus water used stupidly could mean a severe shock or even death. Never touch plugs with wet hands. It is sensible to unplug all appliances when not in use. Young children should not be allowed to use any power equipment. When old enough to be taught its proper use they should do so only under strict supervision.

Electrical equipment and easily laundered fabrics can cut out the miseries of washday. But even the most automatic of machines should be used carefully. Spin dryers should be allowed to stop spinning before you put your hand in otherwise you are likely to break your fingers. Automatic wringers should have a release bar to quickly separate the rollers in emergency, but you should pay full attention to what you are doing as even pinched fingers could cause discomfort. Make sure all surplus water is removed from clothes before hanging in an electric drying cabinet as drips could cause a fuse.

The usual precautions should be taken when using gas in the kitchen. Safety taps should always be used so that the gas cannot be turned by a young child. Most modern appliances have a safety device which turns off the gas should the pilot flame be blown out accidentally. Remember to open the door of the oven before turning on the gas. It could quickly fill with gas and cause an explosion should you open the door when holding a lighted match.

Burns and scalds are often caused by lack of commonsense. Plan your kitchen so that there is no need to walk any distance carrying hot liquids. Position saucepans and kettles with handles and spouts turned inwards so that they cannot be knocked over or pulled down by a small child. A pan guard is not expensive, very easy to fit and could prevent a serious accident. The cooker should not be used for drying clothes.

Care should be taken when frying that the fat does not catch fire. The outside of the pan should be kept clean as a build up of burnt fat could one day catch fire. Use the correct temperature on the hot plate or use a cooking thermometer. Do not overfill the pan. Keep a lid or baking tray handy. If the fat does catch fire put on the lid and this will put out the fire.

Halls are an obvious danger here to all age groups. Good, even lighting is essential, with two way switches within easy reach of the children in the hall and the landing. Many communal dwellings such as blocks of flats are fitted with time switches. These are supposed to leave the light on long enough for the average person to get up or down stairs and then switch off automatically. Unfortunately not everyone can manage to get up or down in the time allowed and this can result in disabled or old people being marooned in the dark in the most dangerous place in the house. In a factory this system would not be permitted, nor should it be allowed in places where people live. The amount of electricity saved is not worth the risk involved.

Staircases should be fitted with balustrades which are firm and easy to grip. An additional safety precaution would be a handrail fixed to the wall side of the stairs. This could be of wood or rope and at the height comfortable to the person most at risk such as an elderly person or a small child. Elderly people and invalids sometimes feel giddy coming downstairs. It helps to count the stairs and to go down one step at a time, even backwards if this gives a greater feeling of security.

Stair coverings should be regularly checked. This can be done when doing the normal cleaning. Carpets and stair rods loosen with use, and carpets fray and curl up at the edges. Never use small mats at the top or bottom of the stairs. All lino covered stairs should be fitted with non slip rubber edges, and the linoleum should not be polished.

Gates fitted at the top and bottom of the stairs restrict access to small children and animals. Children should never be allowed to play on the stairs. No one should be allowed to leave things on the stairs even for a short time.

Do not carry heavy loads on your own. You should always have one hand free to hold on to the bannister. This is especially important if you are carrying a small child as a fall could result in two of you being injured.

Bedrooms

Bedrooms should be places where you can relax completely secure that you are in no danger. But safety cannot be taken for granted even here. The general rules for safety must be adhered to here as much as in any other part of the house. Indeed there is an added danger in that you often do silly things when you are tired, or even half asleep, which you would never do when wide awake. There should be no need to have to turn out the light before getting into bed. A light switch or a table lamp by the bed allows you to see where you are going until you are safely in bed and if you have to get up in the night it should be easy to switch on in the dark.

Bedrooms should be comfortably warm but well ventilated. Gas fires should be turned off before you go to sleep. Electric blankets are very comforting but should be turned off before you get into bed unless they are the low voltage type designed for all night use. Folding or creasing should be avoided and they should never be switched on if at all damp. Regular servicing is important, most makers will undertake this at a reasonable cost. Hot water bottles should have fitted covers especially if they are to be used by an invalid who cannot move easily, or a small child. Faulty bottles should be discarded to avoid risk of scalding.

Night wear should be made of flare free fabrics. Pyjamas are less likely to catch fire then flowing nightdresses. Nightwear should not be so long that you could trip over it. Sloppy slippers are dangerous. Bedroom slippers can be well fitted and still be comfortable and attractive.

Smoking in bed should be discouraged. It is too easy to fall asleep with a lighted cigarette in your hand. The fumes from the smouldering bed clothes could suffocate you before you realised that the bed was on fire. Do not keep sleeping tablets or any other drugs beside the bed. If you are restless or in pain during the night it may be difficult to remember the correct dosage and fatally easy to take an overdose.

Making the beds is a routine job for the homemaker. Make it

as easy as possible by fitting casters so that the bed can be rolled instead of pushed. Get help when turning the mattress. If the bed is a low one kneel down to tuck in the covers. Bending can be tiring especially when there are a number of beds to be made.

Bathroom

Falls and electric shocks are the main danger but with care you can cut these to the minimum. Surfaces that are hard and smooth can easily become slippery when wet. Avoid polished floors and slippery rugs. A large cork mat is safer than one of flimsy towelling.

Baths can be fitted with handgrips. Non-skid rubber pads can be used in the bath to prevent slipping. A shower cabinet can be used with confidence by people who have difficulty getting into a normal bath. A seat could be used to make it even more comfortable.

Electrical accidents should not happen, but because people are careless the combined effect of water and electrical current has often proved fatal. Never take portable electrical appliances into the bathroom. Electric razors should only be used with a socket designed specially for their safe use. All other electrical equipment should be fixed. It should only be possible to switch them on outside the bathroom or with pull cords. This includes lighting and heating. The heater should be fixed high up on the wall away from the bath.

Gas heaters should be checked regularly. You should not take a bath while the geyser is alight. Make sure you have sufficient ventilation.

Glass containers can look attractive but are dangerous. Glass splinters are difficult to detect. Plastic may not look so elegant, but is safer in the bathroom.

A warm moist bathroom is not the best place to keep medicines but should you do so they should be locked up and the key put out of reach of children. Throw away unwanted medicine or pills into the fire or down the lavatory. Razor blades should be put into a safe container and disposed of as soon as possible. Little boys are fascinated by shaving and quite likely to try it for themselves if razors are left within reach.

Cleaning fluids should not be within reach of children. Do not mix different cleaning fluids or bleaches as these can cause very dangerous fumes.

In an emergency you may need to get into a locked bathroom should a child be trapped or an adult become unwell. Before this happens it is as well to remove the conventional lock and key or bolt and replace it with a safety lock. The door can then be forced without damaging it.

The Garden

Most people in this country would like a house with a garden. The garden can be used to play, work or just relax according to age and interests. For children it is a place to do daring things and act out wild adventures. The most attractive gardens look as if they 'just happened' but a good deal of planning must go into making them safe for every member of the family.

Many popular shrubs and trees have poison berries. Children are likely to eat them. Find out which shrubs are dangerous. Avoid buying them and dig out any already in the garden.

Pools and streams can look most pleasant but it is possible to drown in even a few inches of water. It would be sensible to fill in or drain pools, and fence off streams while children are small. Pools could also be covered by nets. Rain water butts should be fitted with secure lids. Children should never be allowed to bathe unsupervised and should be taught to swim as soon as possible.

Trees are a wonderful source of adventure when they are big enough to be climbed. Most children can climb safely but it is as well to check branches to make sure they are in good condition. Very old trees should be inspected frequently in case the roots have rotted.

You may find yourself harbouring unwelcome guests in the form of a nest of wasps or of worker bees. The wasps should be destroyed and the bees removed. Do not try to do this yourself. Find out where the nest is then call at your local Town Hall or Council Offices. The Health Department should be able to send an expert to deal with the problem.

Paths and steps should be kept in good condition, even and well illuminated where necessary. You are unlikely to wander around the garden at night but you may need to go to the garden shed, the garage, or the coal shed. It would be as well to be able to do so without tripping over cracks or walking into obstructions.

Steps should have a handrail when necessary and be illuminated where possible. They can be made safer if the edge of each step is shown as a different texture or colour.

Fences and gates should be a protective guard to prevent young children or animals wandering, but they are only efficient if kept in good order and the gates properly fastened.

Garden sheds and garages contain many things attractive to children but liable to cause them harm. They should be locked up and the keys kept out of reach of the children. Do not leave car keys where a child can get hold of them. It is simple enough to start the engine and release the brake. If the car is on a slope the result could be disastrous. If the car is in an enclosed space such as the garage the child could very quickly be overcome by the gas fumes from the exhaust.

Many of the modern tools such as cutters and power drills make gardening and home maintenance fairly easy and enjoyable, but it is as well to remember that they are not toys to be played with by adults or children. Use them carefully. Never allow children to use them even if it might save you a little time or energy. They should be serviced regularly and kept locked up.

Most gardeners use insecticides or fertilizers at some time. Many of these are poisonous. Follow makers instructions as to the strength and time to use them. If fruit or vegetables should not be eaten for a certain length of time after spraying, make a note of this and be sure every member of the family is aware of the fact and the dangers involved. All poisons should be clearly labelled and locked away along with other dangerous substances such as paraffin and petrol.

Ladders should be locked away. This not only makes sure children do not play with them but also prevents someone being tempted to use them to break into the house.

Garden swings need to be checked for rotting ropes, rusty bolts and splintered woodwork. Sandpits should be kept covered, and frequently raked or sifted to remove toys or bottles which may be accidentally buried there.

Finally having checked that the garden is clear of rubbish and safe for the family to use, dispose of broken glass and wire into the dustbin. If you are burning the rest do so in an incinerator away from any trees or building which could catch fire. Stay with the fire until you are sure it has quite burnt out. If in doubt soak it with water before you leave it.

2 First Aid

Remember that First Aid should be just what it says. If anyone does have an accident in the home you will do all you can to relieve pain, deal with very minor injuries, and reassure the victim. If there is the slightest doubt that more expert treatment is needed, you should call the doctor, or an ambulance to get the patient to hospital.

It is a very good idea to take a course in First Aid. You cannot learn this from a book; the best thing is to join a class of practical and theoretical instruction. These are run by the Red Cross and by the St John's Ambulance Association in all parts of the country.

Bleeding

If there is severe bleeding from a limb apply pressure by putting on a pad of gauze and cotton wool and bandaging tightly. If the bleeding persists apply pressure to the artery above the wound and get medical help immediately.

Treat for shock. Do not try to clean the wound. Do not disturb patient. Cover him with a blanket but do not use hot water bottle. Give him a few sips of weak tea. Never give alcohol.

Nose bleeding:
This is seldom serious. Sit the person up with head slightly forward. Loosen clothing around the neck. A cold compress held on the bridge of the nose will usually stop the flow after a few minutes. Should bleeding continue for a long time, or if the nose bleeds frequently it is as well to see a doctor.

Blister
A blister is nature's way of protecting the damaged tissues beneath. Burn blisters should never be punctured. If the blister is caused by rubbing and it is quite small, it is safe to puncture it using a sharp and sterile needle. Pierce carefully, squeeze out the fluid and cover with a dressing.

Broken bones
Do not move the patient but make him comfortable. Immobilise injured part with bandages and sling support. Avoid splints. Get medical help straight away. Treat for shock.

Bruises
These can be made less painful by a cold compress; soak a cloth in really cold water and apply to bruise.

Burns and scalds
If the burn is very slight put immediately in cold water until the stinging stops. Then carefully dry and cover with a light dressing and a bandage.

If the damage is anything more than very trivial, send for a doctor at once, or get the patient to the nearest hospital without delay. While waiting for expert help you can lessen the pain by immersing the part in cold water as above but do not attempt any further treatment. Do not try to remove burnt clothing as this may do further damage to the tissues. The patient may be in shock so treat this first, while waiting for the doctor or ambulance.

Choking
This is caused by food or any other object getting caught in the throat or windpipe. Hold a small child upside down and slap hard on the back between the shoulders. For an older

child slap hard between the shoulders or try to remove the obstruction with your fingers. If this does not work get the person into a car and drive to the nearest doctor or hospital or dial emergency service for an ambulance. Speed is essential.

Cuts

Wash in mild disinfectant such as one teaspoonful Dettol to ½ litre of water. Dry and then cover with a dressing. If the wound is large it may need stitches. You may do more harm than good by washing it. Cover with a clean dry dressing and get the patient to your doctor straight away. Do not ignore even small wounds if soil or rust has got into them. An injection against tetanus may be needed, so see a doctor at once.

Dislocation

When joints are dislocated they usually show deformity, bruising and inability to use the joint. It is at first numb then very painful. Support the limb so that it is immobilised with cushions or rolled up clothing. Call the doctor. Do not move the patient in case the bone is broken.

Electric shock

Switch off current. If this cannot be done drag the person off by means of a wooden walking stick or broom in order to break the contact. Send for a doctor. If breathing has ceased apply artificial respiration.

Eyes

Eye wounds and injuries should always have expert attention. The most you should do is cover the eyes with a light sterile dressing. If a tiny foreign body gets into the eye use an eye bath to wash it out. If this fails, see a doctor.

Fainting

If the person feels faint get him to sit down and bend forward head between knees. He will usually feel better within a few minutes. If the patient has fainted leave him where he is, loosen his clothing and keep him warm. Give as much air as you can. Smelling salts may be used but do not give anything to drink until he is fully conscious. Keep him quiet until he recovers.

Foreign body in the ear

If the foreign body cannot be removed easily with a pair of tweezers you should avoid any inexpert treatment and get the help of your doctor or the casualty department of the hospital. You could do serious and permanent harm whereas the expert using the correct instrument can solve the problem painlessly.

Foreign body in the nose

Again you should only attempt to remove this if you can see it easily. It might be possible to remove it by blowing the nose while closing the other nostril. If this does not work seek expert help.

Gas poisoning

Get the victim out of the gas filled atmosphere into fresh air. Lay him down with his head on one side. If he is not breathing use artificial respiration. Send for a doctor. Keep the patient warm.

Head injuries

A blow on the head can cause concussion. If there is loss of consciousness after such an accident call a doctor and leave the patient where he is. Make him as comfortable as possible and darken the room. Rest and sleep are necessary for recovery.

Insect bites and stings

If the sting is present remove with sterile tweezers or needle. Dab with mild antiseptic solution. There are various creams and lotions available to relieve the discomfort. Your doctor or chemist will advise the most suitable for you. Bee stings are neutralized by ammonia, bicarbonate of soda or washing soda and wasp stings by vinegar or lemon juice. Should the wasp or bee sting be in the mouth; if there is severe swelling; or if there are signs of collapse get medical attention straight away.

Poisoning
Send for the doctor immediately. Keep the patient warm and try to find out the cause of poisoning. Keep any remains of poison and vomit until the doctor arrives.

If there is no burning of the mouth give the patient an emetic of two tablespoons salt in half a pint of warm water every five minutes until vomiting occurs.

If the mouth is burnt do not cause vomiting. Magnesia in water will help. If the cause is unknown, give large quantities of water.

Splinters and Thorns
These should be removed as they are likely to cause irritation and infection. Loosen with a sterilized needle and squeeze out or remove with tweezers. If you find it difficult to persuade a small child to remain still for you to do this put a piece of adhesive plaster over the splinter. You will probably find that next day you can pull off the plaster and the splinter will be attached to it.

Sprains
These show bruising and swelling and severe pain on trying to move the limb. Support the injured part and apply cold compresses. Call the doctor.

Sunburn
This can be painful. Treat with frequent applications of calamine. The patient should rest as he is likely to have a headache and feel generally unwell. If the burn is at all severe see the doctor.

Swallowed objects
Small smooth objects like buttons and small marbles usually pass quite harmlessly through the body within two or three days. Should the object be sharp or pointed or should there be severe pain or sickness get medical attention straight away. Do not give anything to eat in the hope of forcing or washing it down.

Toothache

Soak a piece of cotton wool in oil of cloves and push this into the cavity. Give the patient soluble aspirin (the dose according to instructions on the bottle) and arrange to see a dentist as soon as possible.

Vomiting

This is nature's way of getting rid of something which does not agree with the body. If poisoning is suspected or the vomiting continues for any time call a doctor.

Artificial Respiration

If the casualty appears to have stopped breathing, remove dentures (if any) and see that air passages are clear. Begin artificial respiration as quickly as you can, continue until the patient recovers or medical help arrives.

Mouth to mouth method (sometimes called the kiss of life)

1 Lift the patient's head right back and the jaw wide open.

2 Take a deep breath and breathe it into the patient's mouth with force for an adult and gently for a small child. There is enough oxygen in this air to revive the patient.

3 Lean back, take another deep breath and repeat.

4 If you feel giddy slow down but keep at it until the patient recovers or help comes.

This is the better method as it can be used even by an untrained person. If you find the whole idea objectionable you will soon overcome this feeling in an emergency.

The Holger Neilson method

1 Place patient face down on a flat surface with forehead supported on his folded arms.

2 Bend down on one knee and put hands on lower part of shoulder blades.

3 Keeping your arms straight, rock forward gently, without applying pressure until your arms are vertical to cause expiration.

4 Rock slowly back sliding hands down patient's arms

almost to elbows at the same time raise his arms and pull on them to cause inspiration.

5 Repeat these movements for as long as possible.

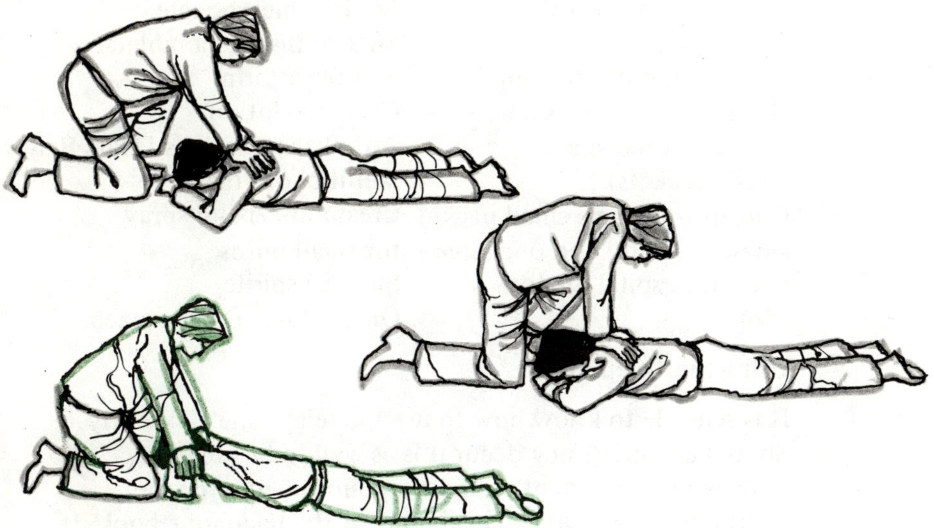

The Medicine Cabinet

The medicine cabinet should be kept stocked with the equipment essential for emergency first aid. There should be one section for drugs and medicines and another for poisons and external applications. The cabinet should be locked and the key put in a place out of reach of the children and preferably known only to grown ups.

The cabinet should be turned out at regular intervals, and any left over medicines and pills should be thrown away into the fire or down the W.C.

Many families keep the medicine cabinet in the bathroom but it is in fact not the best place as the heat and steam may penetrate the cabinet and spoil the contents. Most accidents happen in the living area of the house during the day.

The contents will vary according to the needs of the family but the list which follows may be used as a guide for the average home.

Clinical thermometer
Eyebath
Graduated medicine glass
Scissors
Pair of fine tweezers
Safety pins
Elastic adhesive dressings
Bandages 1, 2 and 3 inch
Gauze (several small sterile packets)
Cotton wool, one small packet, surgical quality and one large packet, hospital quality
Lint
Crepe bandages (for sprains)
Two slings
Proprietary antiseptic such as Dettol, Milton or Cetavlon
Sodium bicarbonate
Milk of magnesia tablets
Soluble aspirin
Calamine lotion
An inhalant such as Friars Balsom
Menthol ointment
Cream or aerosol spray for small burns
Surgical spirits
Oil of cloves for toothache

Using the Telephone

It is sensible to know how to use the telephone efficiently. Should an emergency occur it is as well to be able to act quickly and confidently. Make a point of studying the instructions given at the beginning of the telephone book. If you do not have a telephone at home it would be worth spending a little time studying the instruction book in a public call box. Choose a time when the telephone is unlikely to be needed.

Learn how to make a call from both a private phone and a public call box.

How to make a call

1 Make sure you know the number.

2 Lift the receiver. Listen for the dialling tone.

3 Dial the number. If your telephone has no dial just ask the operator for the number.

4 Wait for another tone.
   (a) Ringing tone, (burr burr) the number is being called.
   (b) Engaged tone, (repeated single note), try again a few minutes later.

(c) Number unobtainable (steady note), replace receiver recheck the number and redial.

5 If your telephone is not automatic the operator will tell you if the number is engaged or unobtainable.

6 When you are connected with your number give your own name and ask for the person to whom you wish to speak. Speak clearly and slowly. Remember that the person the other end cannot see you so it is pointless trying to express yourself with gesticulations or facial expressions.

7 At the end of the call make sure the telephone is replaced securely.

To call the operator for emergency services (fire, police, ambulance, coastguard, lifeboat and rescue stations)

Dial 999 or as shown on the dial label.
On a non-dial phone lift receiver and wait.
Tell the operator which service you want.
Give your exchange and number.
Wait until the emergency service answers.
Give them the address where help is needed and any other necessary information.

If you look at the instruction panel in a public call box you will find the exact location of the box. This will help in case of a nearby road accident.

Do not make emergency calls for non-urgent calls. Never call out the fire brigade, police or a doctor as a practical joke. Somebody might be really needing their help just at the time you are being entertained.

Do not hesitate to call them in a real emergency.

3 Health of the Family

The pre-school child

During these years the child is growing rapidly both physically and mentally. He needs plenty of sleep, a sensible diet and plenty of exercise.

Training in good habits is important in these first few years. These habits will stand him in good stead throughout his life. He should be encouraged to do things for himself so that he becomes confident and resourceful. Good habits of eating and sleeping and cleanliness are best formed at this time as they are accepted easily with little of the rebellion which might arise should you try to impose them later.

Before he starts school he should know how to wash himself, to go to the lavatory on his own and to dress himself. These skills must be taught gradually and patiently. As with every other stage of learning there are bound to be set backs but the mother should try not to show irritation.

The school child

The small child starting school is exposed to a variety of hazards. If he has been isolated from children other than those in his family he may not have built up a natural immunity to a variety of illnesses. If the recommended immunisation schedule has been caried out he will be protected against the more serious infections.

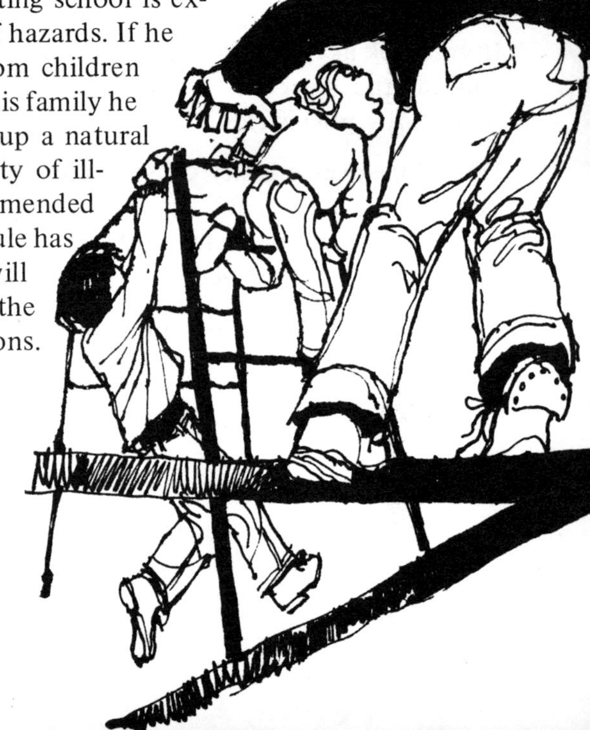

His routine will be different and more arduous than that of his pre-school days. His mother must make sure he gets enough rest and is having a suitable diet. Some children do not like eating at school or find the quantity of the meal insufficient. If this is so the mother must make sure the deficiency is made up either with sensible snacks to be eaten at playtime or by increasing the size of breakfast and every other meal. Eating sweets and chocolate during the day should be discouraged. They dull the appetite for meals and as the child is unlikely to clean his teeth after eating them encourage tooth decay.

The older school child faces increasing physical mental and emotional strains. He will be better equipped to cope with them if he is in good health. A sensible diet plenty of sleep and plenty of exercise in the fresh air should be a help in attaining this.

Toys

Children need toys for both enjoyment and education. They need them to help develop sense of colour, size, shape and touch but if the child is to get the full benefit of his toys it is essential that they should be safe for him to play with.

1 They should be suitable for his age group.
2 There should be no sharp or rough edges.
3 There should be no detachable parts small enough for the child to swallow or push up his nostrils or into his ear.
4 If the toy is pulled apart there should be no sharp attachments exposed like metal wires or hooks.
5 All stuffings for soft toys should be hygienic and preferably washable.
6 The paint used to coat the toy should not contain lead or any other poisonous substance.

The British Standards Safety Code 3443 of 1968 lists the standards of safety requirements for toys and playthings. The Consumer Council has published a very useful booklet *About Buying Toys* which gives detailed advice about toys suitable for each age group from birth to twelve years of age.

Protecting the young child against infection

The advances in child care have reduced many of the illnesses which frequently threatened the lives of infants in the past. The doctor or health visitor can advise on protective measures which reduce the risk of poliomylitis, diphtheria, whooping cough, tetanus and smallpox. The immunisation can be carried out at the clinic or by the family doctor.

Recommended Immunisation Schedule

Approximate Age	*Vaccine*
3 months 4 months 5 months	Diphtheria/Whooping cough/Tetanus injection plus Poliomyelitis vaccine by mouth
12 months	Smallpox vaccination
18 months	Diphtheria/Whooping cough/Tetanus injection plus Poliomyelitis vaccine by mouth
5 years	Diphtheria/Tetanus injection plus Poliomyelitis vaccine by mouth
During last year in Junior School	Diphtheria/Tetanus injection
During first year in Secondary School	Re-vaccination against Smallpox
During second year in Secondary School	B.C.G. vaccination against Tuber-culosis

An infection which may be mild in an adult or even a school child could prove serious if passed on to a small child. Any-one with any infection, even a slight cold should keep away from small children. Children should not be encouraged to kiss or be kissed.

Personal articles should not be shared. Even very small children can be taught to use only their own tooth brushes, towels, handkerchief and combs. They can easily be trained to drink only from clean cups and not to share ice creams, lolly-pops or drinking straws. Prevention is better than cure. Every effort should be made to prevent exposing a small child to infection of any sort.

General rules for keeping the family healthy

1 Every member of the family should have a diet suitable to his age, size, work etc.

2 Each person should have sufficient rest. This will vary for each person but it should be enough to allow them to cope with all normal activities without being overtired.

3 Regular exercise, this will keep circulation and muscles in good condition.

4 Regular bowel action ensures the elimination of waste products from the body.

5 The skin should be kept clean by a daily bath or wash down. The use of a deodorant by men as well as women, should be encouraged.

6 Hair should be kept clean.

7 Feet need regular attention. Keep feet clean and nails trimmed. Choose shoes and stockings carefully.

8 Teeth should be cleaned regularly. Regular check ups with the dentist can help to prevent serious dental troubles.

9 Clothes should be changed frequently, especially those worn next to the skin.

10 The home environment should be clean, dry and well ventilated and at a comfortable temperature.

11 The family should have plenty of fresh air.

12 Should any member of the family become ill care should be taken not to spread infection.

4 Care of Mother and Baby

The special care of mother and baby should begin long before the child is born. This should be considered from the time the woman first suspects that she might be pregnant. It must be stressed that pregnancy is not an illness. Indeed the woman will probably feel extremely fit during this time if she is taking care of her health. The extra care is to ensure a safe confinement and a healthy baby.

It is important for her to consult a doctor as soon as possible. The doctor will be able to confirm that she is really pregnant and the approximate date of the birth. It will be necessary now to decide whether the baby is to be born in hospital or at home. The safety of the mother and baby must override all other considerations. Various reasons may indicate the need for hospitalisation. Should the doctor recommend this it would be foolish not to accept his advice.

The doctor will arrange for her to attend the booking clinic of the hospital concerned where a bed will be reserved for the confinement and a full medical examination carried out. The expectant mother will also be given advice on the various benefits due to her, the vitamin and cheap milk supply. She can get help from the medical social worker to deal with problems related to other members of the family such as small children who will need to be cared for while she is away.

If the baby is to be born at home it is the midwife and the doctor who will give this care and help.

The clinic doctor or the family doctor will want to see the expectant mother at regular intervals and she should not miss any of these visits. It is essential that he should be able to keep a regular check on her health. He will then be able to recognise and deal with any troubles before they have a bad effect on the mother or the baby. It also helps the mother to get to know the people looking after her. Most ante-natal clinics are run in a friendly helpful way. This enables the mother to relax and ask any questions about anything which may worry her. The doctors and midwives can then allay her fears. She should not listen to 'old wives tales', these are usually told by ignorant people who like to feel important. They are seldom accurate.

Most clinics run classes of exercises for expectant mothers. These exercises help to train the muscles used in giving birth, so keeping discomfort to the minimum. The women also learn what to expect at each stage of the confinement so that they are spared the anxiety of not knowing just what is happening.

The midwife and the clinic nurses will usually give advice on planning the baby's layette and on maternity clothes. It is not a good idea to wear maternity clothes too soon but she should plan to have several outfits so that she can still look attractive when pregnancy is far advanced. Maternity clothes can be bought or made in so many styles and fabrics that it is quite unnecessary to look dowdy or to need to spend an excessive amount of money.

Attention to diet is important. The amount of proteins and foods containing vitamins, calcium and iron, should be increased gradually to supply the needs of the developing child. Too much carbohydrate food should be avoided as this may cause overweight.

The diet should include a litre of milk daily and plenty of fresh fruit and vegetables, especially citrus fruits. She should eat plenty of eggs, cheese and butter. The expectant mother is allowed 3·5 litres of milk a week at a reduced price. This is for her use and should not be shared by the family. She should also take fish liver oil, Vitamin A and D tablets and the concentrated orange juice. These are all obtainable for a nominal price at the welfare foods distribution centre (usually at the ante-natal clinic). She should continue to take these after the baby is born even though she may feel fit.

Digestive upsets at this time are seldom serious. Morning sickness can be minimised by having a cup of tea and dry toast or a biscuit before getting up. Avoid fried or fatty foods while the problem lasts. Alcohol and smoking should be avoided. No sane mother would give her baby alcohol, nicotine or other drugs. Many forget that the unborn child shares the mother's blood supply and is affected by anything she may drink eat or smoke. She should not take any medicines or tablets other than those prescribed by the doctor.

Most of the minor illnesses that the mother might contract should have little effect on the child. For her own sake the mother should not leave herself at risk of catching any infection. German measles is the one virus infection which should be particularly avoided during the first three months. If she thinks she has been exposed to the risk of catching this infection she should tell her doctor immediately. He can take steps to protect her so that the baby is not harmed.

While regular exercise is important she should not get overtired. She should avoid lifting and pulling heavy weights or unnecessary stretching. Medium heeled shoes will be more comfortable than very high or flat heels. These should be properly fitted to minimise the dangers of losing balance and falling.

Plenty of rest is essential and this should be taken with the feet up to prevent feet and legs becoming swollen. This is an ideal time to make the layette and to plan the nursery. If there are other small children the mother could use this time to prepare them to accept the coming baby. If they become interested in the preparations and feel they are helping there is less likely to be undue jealousy when the baby arrives.

After the baby is born the midwife will continue to attend the mother and baby so long as she is needed. If the baby is born in hospital the average length of stay is now about seven days. About 12% of mothers are discharged within fortyeight hours of delivery to the care of the family doctor and mid-wife.

The health visitor will call on the mother in her own home. She is trained to help with all the problems involved in the care of young children. She is usually in attendance at the maternal and child health centre. The majority of mothers take their babies here for regular health checks and advice in all matters concerning the baby's welfare.

About six weeks after birth the mother is given a post-natal examination by the hospital or family doctor to confirm that she has returned to normal health and activity. She should continue to eat sensibly and take the vitamin supplements. Looking after a small baby can be very tiring so it is essential that she should get enough rest.

Most women experience periods of post-natal depression. This is normal and will quickly pass. Sometimes a mother is distressed to find that, although she may have wanted and looked forward to having a baby, she is overwhelmed by the responsibility involved. Again this is a perfectly normal reaction. She will usually find that as she gets to know and to learn to love the child most of these fears will pass. At this stage it is sensible to do the minimum of housework and learn to enjoy the baby rather than have a perfect house with a worried mother and fretful child.

The Layette

When planning the layette the main consideration should be the comfort of the baby. He will be unaware of colour or fashion but will be miserable if a fabric irritates his skin or a garment is too tight. Garments should be few but warm. Most baby clothes are constantly being washed so one must choose a fabric or yarn which will tolerate this without shrinking or becoming rough. Many of the man made fibres are spun and woven into warm, soft, and easily laundered fabrics. While the initial cost may be a little higher this is made up for by the longer wear and ease of laundering. Synthetic fibres dry very quickly so fewer garments will be needed than in a layette made up mainly of woollen garments.

Have the very minimum of first size garments. The baby grows out of these very quickly. It is a popular size for people to give as presents to the new baby so he is unlikely to be short of clothes. Simple styles are more comfortable than complicated fussy clothes, and they are also easier for the mother to look after. The fastenings should be kept as simple as possible. Avoid ribbons threaded through necklines as these could get caught and pulled tight causing the child to choke. Baby is more comfortable if he is dressed while lying on his tummy so it is better to have fastenings at the back. The type of garments one chooses will also be influenced by the climate of the area, the time of the year the baby is born and the temperature in the home. An all-in-one garment in a stretch fabric, plus napkin, is an easy and sensible way to dress baby.

The Nursery

Plan the nursery for safety, comfort and cleanliness. The nursery is often planned before the first child is born. It should be remembered that the baby soon becomes an active toddler and then a lively schoolchild. The room may eventually have to be shared by several children. Frequent changes of furniture can prove very expensive. Sturdy, well designed furniture can be adapted to the needs of each group.

If possible the room should face south to get as much sunlight as possible. The room should be well ventilated, without draughts and one that can be easily warmed. For the first few months of the baby's life the room temperature must be kept above 18°C. Remember that it is a legal obligation, apart from commonsense, to have a guard in front of any fire in rooms used by children. The window should be fitted with vertical bars not more than 8 cms apart. The decoration of the room will depend on personal preference and the money available. All surfaces and furnishings should be smooth and easily cleaned. Lead paints must not be used as this can prove dangerous and even fatal if chewed off by the child.

Make sure there is sufficient storage space for all the baby's clothes and equipment but avoid overcrowding. A sturdy table and a comfortable chair should be provided. A tea trolley can be adapted to hold all the baby's toilet articles.

A crib or cradle may be used while the baby is really small; a cot with high sides will be needed when the baby is about six months and able to move on his own. Make sure both crib and cot are really safe and cannot be collapsed by a lively child. The locking device holding the cot sides should be secure and child proof. The filling bars should be no more than 8 centimetres apart.

The mattress should be really firm. It is better not to use a pillow. A baby can easily be smothered by a soft pillow. Covers should be light and warm. Do not use plastic mattress covers as they can cling to the face and cause suffocation.

The baby should never be taken into his parents' bed to sleep as there is a real danger of them turning over on to him in sleep and suffocating him. A proper crib or cot may not be available because of cost, or while staying away from home. It would be better to improvise with the pram, to use a drawer or even a large box rather than have him sharing a bed with an adult.

It would be impossible to watch over the baby every moment of the day. As soon as the baby starts to crawl it is sensible to have a playpen. This could be used in the house or in the garden.

The pram should have a non tip device and really efficient brakes. A pram harness will be needed when the baby is four or five months old. A pram net is essential if the baby is to be left alone in the garden. This is a protection against cats or other animals which might jump onto the pram. As for the cot a firm mattress is essential. A pillow should only be used when the baby is awake and sitting up. If the pram is to be used for both a baby and a toddler a seat can be bought to fit on to the pram. Care must be taken that this does not upset the balance.

Feeding Baby

When possible baby should be breastfed. The milk contains the correct proportions of nutrients including antitoxins needed to help fight disease. It is a convenient and clean method of feeding. Bottle feeding may be necessary as the only method or as a supplement to breastfeeding.

It may be necessary to try several types of baby food before finding the most suitable formula. The manufacturers give full instructions for making up the food. The quantity given depends on the weight of the baby rather than the age. The clinic staff will help and advise on this as it is important that the baby is feeding happily as soon as possible.

All the apparatus used for mixing the food and the feeding bottles must be properly sterilized before use. It is possible to buy inexpensive kits to do this efficiently so that there is no chance of feeding baby with germs. Test the temperature of the feed by sprinkling a little on the back of your hand. It should feel neither hot nor cold. If it is too hot cool it under a running cold tap.

Bottle fed babies need regular daily amounts of Vitamin C and D. The Vitamin C can be given in the form of orange juice, blackcurrent juice or rose-hip syrup added to the feed or diluted with water and given in the bottle between feeds. Vitamin D as halibut or liver oil is best given from a spoon as it clings to the side of the bottle and may not be taken in with the food.

Baby should never be left alone in his pram or cot to take his bottle feed. Not only does he need the reassurance of being cuddled while he is fed but there is a real danger of him bringing back his food and being suffocated by it.

The rate of growth varies from one child to another. So long as the baby is healthy and contented there is no need to worry if the increase is very small. If the baby is putting on a lot of weight but is often sick or restless he may be getting too much food or too rich a mixture.

Though it is easier to organise the day if the baby keeps to a regular routine there is no need to be too rigid. Do not wake the baby for a feed or allow him to cry with hunger.

Weaning may start as early as two months old with two or three teaspoons of a smooth cereal being given before the milk feed. As the baby grows and becomes more active he needs more iron, vitamins and other nutrients essential to proper development. These cannot be supplied by milk alone so other foods must be added to the diet. Weaning should be done very gradually so that the baby learns to enjoy the new textures and flavours. Good eating habits can be learned now. Try to make sugary foods unimportant and encourage a liking for a wide range of fruits vegetables and protein foods. By the time the baby is about a year old he will be having food similar to the rest of the family. Feeding times will gradually fit in with family meals.

Teething

This can be a time of fretfulness. The baby will be comforted by having something hard to chew such as a teething ring or a hard rusk. He may like small pieces of cheese or apple but make sure he is not left alone with these as he may try to swallow too large a piece. As the teeth come through the gum they can cause considerable inflammation and a temperature. If there is severe pain and distress it would be as well to refer to a doctor.

Bathing the baby

Bath time for the baby may either be in the evening to soothe and settle the baby during the night or at mid morning. Morning bathing is often preferred because the mother is less likely to be interrupted by other members of the family needing attention.

Get everything ready before you start and make sure the room is warm and free of draught. Use a screen if necessary. Many women prefer to put the baby on a table rather than to hold him on their laps. This is a sensible precaution if the mother is still a little nervous or if the baby is very active. Make sure you are not wearing any brooches or anything which might scratch the baby.

Equipment needed
Bath, low chair, bucket with lid for napkins, chamber pot. Toilet articles including cotton wool. Warm towels. Clean warm clothes. Hot water.

1 Shut windows and arrange screen.
2 Fill bath quarter full with cold water. Never put hot water in first. This could result in an accident if you are called away.
3 Add hot water. Test temperature with elbow or with a bath thermometer – not with your hand.
4 Protect yourself with a plastic or towelling apron.
5 Do not sit where direct heat will be on the baby's head.
6 Undress baby as far as his vest.
7 Remove dirty napkin. Put into bucket and cover with lid.
8 Hold baby out and then clean him up with soft tissue or cotton wool.
9 Cover baby with warm towel.
10 Clean eyes with cotton wool wrung out in water. Use a fresh piece of wool for each eye.
11 Clean ears with dry wool.
12 Tickle nose with a little dry wool so that the baby sneezes and clears the nasal passages. Clean nose.
13 Wash hair. Lightly soap hand and rub it over the baby's head. Support the head on your arm and hold it over the edge of the bath. Rinse well. Dry.
14 Wash face gently. Dry gently but thoroughly.
15 Take off vest and soap baby's body.
16 Put baby into the bath supporting his back with your arm. Rinse properly. Most babies like being in the bath and will enjoy kicking and splashing for a few minutes.
17 Take baby out and wrap him in a towel. Dry thoroughly

especially in the folds of the skin. Powder lightly.

18 Put on vest.

19 Hold him out again. Clean up with cotton wool or tissue.

20 Fold napkin, lay baby flat on napkin and pin up the napkin securely at the waist.

21 Remove towel and finish dressing baby.

22 Feed the baby.

Washing baby clothes

1 Use only the mildest detergents, or soap powder or flakes.
2 Rinse clothes thoroughly. Avoid using bleach but if it is really essential make sure that all traces of bleach are thoroughly washed and rinsed out of the fabric.
3 Do not starch a garment which touches the skin. Spray starches could be used on isolated areas such as skirts of dresses and coats or on brims of summer bonnets.
4 Clothes should be dried and aired thoroughly.

Napkins

These need special care. Napkins should be changed frequently so that the baby is comfortable and does not develop sore skin and rashes. Dirty napkins should be dealt with at once and all napkins should be washed on the day they are used.

1 Remove as much soil as possible and put to steep in cold water. Napkin liners or even paper handkerchiefs used inside the napkin can help reduce the number of soiled napkins.
2 Put to steep in a covered pail of cold water to which you have added a suitable antiseptic.
3 Wet napkins should be rinsed out and then put to soak in a separate lot of water.
4 If possible use a washing machine to wash the napkins. This enables you to use hotter water than the hand can bear.

5 Use a mild detergent or soap flakes. Make sure the napkins are rinsed at least three times in clear water. A fabric softening product may be used in the last rinse.

6 It is not necessary to boil the napkins every time to keep them white. This should be done however if the baby suffers from napkin rash.

7 If possible dry napkins in the open air.

8 Air well.

The task of washing napkins can be made much easier if you have the use of washing machines and drying equipment. Many areas have napkin laundry service while there are a variety of types of disposable napkins on the market. Make sure that it is safe to dispose of the latter down the W.C. before doing so, as you may otherwise find yourself having to deal with blocked drains.

Dummies

Dummies are probably the cause of more arguments than any other aspect of baby care. While it would obviously be stupid to encourage a baby to suck a dummy, many are comforted by them. The main objection is that many mothers are not sufficiently fussy about the cleanliness of the dummy. As much care should be taken in sterilizing them as for the feeding bottles. If the dummy is to be used, it would be as well to have several so that a clean one is always available. The dummy should be attached to a ribbon which can be pinned to the baby's clothes. This would prevent it falling to the ground and being used again in an unclean condition. Do not tie the ribbon around the neck as it could get caught up and be pulled too tight.

5 Care of the Elderly

'Old age' does not suddenly happen to a person nor does it come at any particular birthday. People vary considerably. There are problems to be met at every stage of life. Those of the later years can be overcome or eased with a little preparation and help.

Elderly people should be encouraged to continue an active life for as long as possible. Retirement from work should not be regarded as the end of usefulness but rather as a time of well earned leisure and enjoyment. It is important to keep in contact with friends and to go out as often as possible. Sitting at home can become a habit and it is very easy to be cut off from people. It is as well to prepare well in advance by developing interests and hobbies which can be carried on in later years.

Most older people like to retain independence for as long as possible. They prefer to be in their own homes with their own possessions. At first all they may need is companionship. If this is given readily by relatives and friends the more practical assistance needed later will be more easily accepted. The older person will accept his limitations without losing his dignity.

The risk of accidents increases with age mainly because sense of sight hearing and smell become less acute. The chief danger is from falls. All normal precautions against accidents should be taken. There are also ways to minimise the special problems of the elderly.

1 Furniture may be modified to make life easier. A low bed is easier to get in and out of than a high one and saves harm, should falls out of bed occur.

2 Most old people prefer chairs with high seats and arms to give support when getting up. It is sensible to provide a chair in the bedroom and bathroom. Giddiness is then less likely to occur while washing, dressing and undressing.

3 Handrails in lavatory and bathroom and on the stairs give considerable assistance. When going downstairs it helps to take one step at a time. Giddiness is less likely to occur if one goes down backwards facing the stairs.

4 Old people should leave bathroom and lavatory doors unlocked in case they fall. Their privacy can be maintained by providing an 'Occupied' sign to hang on the door. If this is not practical safety locks should be fitted.

5 A shower cabinet with a stool could prove safer than a bath.

6 Fire guards are essential.

7 Gas and electric appliances should be checked regularly. The Gas Council has developed a cooker for handicapped people which could prove useful for the elderly infirm.

8 Articles in regular use should be stored at a height which is easily reached.

The elderly should be encouraged to take some exercise each day. A daily walk should be encouraged but it should not be so long or at such a pace as to be tiring. Activity stimulates the circulation and strengthens bones and muscles. Many old people become housebound because of painful feet. The majority of local authorities have a chiropody service. The doctor can arrange for skilled treatment, free of charge if necessary. Well fitting shoes and slippers are essential and they should be kept in good repair. Regular bathing of the feet and changes of sock or stockings also help.

While exercise is important so is plenty of rest. A sofa or a comfortable chair with a footstool will allow short rests to be taken with feet up. All slight infirmities should be noticed and treated before they develop into more serious problems. Any discomforts or disorders should be discussed with the family doctor. Many older people find that their sight and hearing can be helped with suitable spectacles or hearing aids. Teeth or dentures should be checked frequently as food which is not properly chewed may cause indigestion.

Elderly people are affected by extremes of temperature. They must be kept warm in winter. Clothing should be light and warm. Guard against draughts which may cause attacks of fibrositis or rheumatism. Bedrooms must be kept warm. At the slightest sign of respiratory infection the temperature must not be allowed to drop below 15°C.

They are also susceptible to a condition known as hypothermia. Through lack of warmth and food the body temperature drops. Apathy and confusion result. The sufferer does not realise he is cold and hungry so does nothing to remedy it. This is an extremely dangerous condition and can prove fatal if medical aid is not given straight away. Fuel is expensive. It may be necessary to make up a bed in the living room in order to ensure a safe temperature.

An elderly person who is healthy should be able to eat the same foods he has eaten all his life. He will have learned from experience which foods do not agree with him. The nutritional needs remain unchanged. The quantity of energy foods may slightly be reduced as activity decreases. Older people often find it difficult to cope with large meals and prefer smaller meals at more frequent intervals.

Plenty of liquids, fresh fruit and at least half a litre of milk should be included in the daily diet. Because the older person spends so much time indoors there is likely to be a shortage of Vitamin D but this can be made up by using margarine.

Protein foods should be served twice a day to counteract the effect of tissue breakdown which increases with age.

Old people living with families do not normally suffer from lack of food. They are involved in the normal household routine including meals. It is when they are living alone that the problem arises. They may find it takes too much effort to prepare a meal or even just forget to eat. Many of them, especially men, just do not know how to cook a balanced meal. Many local authorities and various voluntary bodies organise cookery classes for retired people. Lessons are given in preparing meals of suitable quantity, food value and cost. Dishes which can be prepared, cooked and served easily such as casseroles, milk puddings, steamed foods, boiled eggs, cheese and canned fish are very useful. Tinned foods need little effort to prepare but make sure the tin opener is one which can be used easily and safely.

Many local authorities provide a 'meals on wheels' service. This provides a hot meal several times a week delivered to the old person's home at a nominal charge.

There are other home services provided by the local authority for elderly people and also by voluntary bodies. The family doctor can arrange for the health visitor to call. She can be invaluable in organising help as necessary.

1 The 'home help' service provides domestic help.
2 Some local authorities have organised people who will sit with an elderly or sick patient throughout the night.
3 The home nurse can visit an elderly patient who is ill at home. She may bathe the patient, give injections or change dressings as advised by the doctor. This service is a great comfort to the patient and to the family. An increasing number of home nurses are now men.
4 Some authorities provide help with the laundry.

The family doctor can call on the full range of medical services. Geriatric units specialise in the treatment of old people, in hospital or as out-patients.

There are a number of voluntary organisations who will help the elderly. These services range from visiting and performing small tasks like shopping and getting in coal, to arranging for holidays.

The Old Peoples Welfare Committee or the Medical Officer of Health should be able to give information about what other services are available. Every effort should be made to keep the elderly happy, in good health, and active members of the community.

6 Home Nursing

With the discovery of the many 'miracle' drugs and modern methods of dealing with illness one seldom has to deal with patients who are bedridden for any length of time. With most illnesses the emphasis is on getting the patient up and out of bed as soon as possible. However mild or serious the illness may be careful nursing can do much to lessen the discomfort of the patient.

As the nurse you are expected to follow the doctor's instructions exactly and to keep the patient comfortable and relaxed. If necessary you should cut down your other work or get help with it. It is important not to attempt to do too much. You may overtax yourself and be of little value to the patient. Make sure you get sufficient rest and that you eat sensibly. An exhausted nurse is liable to become another patient.

The sickroom should be arranged so as to be as comfortable as possible for the patient and the nurse. It should be easy to clean and with the minimum of furniture. This should include a really comfortable chair for the nurse which the

patient can use during convalescence. This may take a little thought and energy but is well worth it especially if the illness lasts more than a few days. It may be convenient to move the patient to a downstairs room. He will feel less isolated from the family and you will be saved the strain of running up and down stairs.

Position the bed carefully. This should be out of draughts. If necessary use a screen to ensure this. A screen can be improvised from a clothes-horse and a blanket. Room lighting and windows should not be facing the patient as glare from these can be tiring. It is easier to nurse a patient in a single bed than a double bed especially if he cannot move without help. Choose the highest bed possible so that the nurse does not have to keep bending over to deal with the patient.

A bed table or a large invalid tray is very useful. A large tray or piece of wood could easily be adapted by the addition of short legs or by resting it on pillows put either side of the patient. The local Health Department and the local branch of the British Red Cross Society will lend a variety of nursing aids from bedrests to invalid chairs. These could make a great deal of difference to the comfort of the patient especially in the case of a lengthy illness.

Bed clothes should be light and warm. A thermostatically controlled electric overblanket provides an even heat at a comfortable temperature with very little weight.

When possible use easily laundered sheets and blankets as they may need to be changed frequently. Non-iron sheets and nylon blankets can be washed at home and be ready to use again in a short time.

If the patient is very ill you may have to change the lower sheet without removing him from the bed. This is not as difficult as it may seem.

1 Close windows and doors and make sure that the room is warm.
2 Make sure that clean linen is ready for use.

3 Strip the bed leaving the patient with one pillow.

4 Roll the patient to one side of the bed.

5 Untuck the dirty sheet and roll it lengthwise down the bed as close to the patient as possible.

6 Put on the clean sheet. Tuck it firmly down the side, smooth over the half of the half of the bed and make a roll of the excess next to the roll of dirty sheet.

7 Roll the patient carefully over to the clean side of the bed.

8 Remove the dirty sheet and tuck in the clean one.

9 Remake the bed.

Make sure there are enough pillows or a backrest to support the patient comfortably. A firm pillow under the knees will stop him slipping down in the bed. If the bedclothes feel heavy on the legs pillows can be used to take off some of the weight. Do not tuck in the bedclothes too tightly unless the patient prefers the bed made this way.

You should make sure your patient does not have to stay in one position for too long. This is one of the causes of bed-sores. They will develop very quickly if the patient is very thin or cannot move on his own. A good nurse will try to make sure these do not happen as they are slow to heal and very uncomfortable for the patient.

The danger points are the base of the spine, the elbows, heels, hips and ankles. Gently massage these areas several times a day. Rub in a little surgical spirits and dust lightly with talcum. Keep the skin clean and dry. Silicone cream rubbed on to the skin will help to prevent soreness particularly if the patient is perspiring heavily or is incontinent.

You will make sure that all the normal toilet procedures are carried out and that teeth are cleaned regularly. A blanket bath efficiently carried out can help to freshen and relax the patient.

1 Collect everything needed, toilet articles, clean nightwear and clean bed linen. You will need two thin blankets or

two large towels, which should be warmed on a radiator or in front of a fire.

2 Prepare plenty of hot water so that the patient is not chilled if the water cools quickly.

3 Close the windows and see that the room is comfortably warm for the patient.

4 Remove all top bedclothes folding them methodically so that no time will be lost in remaking the bed.

5 Remove night clothes. Cover the patient with one of the warmed blankets and roll him on to the other warmed blanket.

6 Wash and dry the patient thoroughly in the following order – face, arms, chest, abdomen, back. Dust with talcum powder. Uncover only the part of the body you are washing and cover up again as soon as you have finished. Wash legs and feet.

7 Make sure you dry the patient thoroughly. He may prefer to do this for himself and should be allowed to do so if he can, unless he has been ordered complete rest by the doctor.

8 Remove blankets and put on clean nightwear.

9 Remake the bed.

10 Brush and comb hair. See that teeth are cleaned.

11 Remember that this may tire the patient so you should now allow him to rest for a while.

During illness the hair is apt to become sticky and lifeless. For a short illness you will be able to keep the hair clean by regular gentle brushing. Excessive oil can be removed with a pad soaked in eau-de-cologne. If necessary you can shampoo the hair while the patient remains in bed. The patient lies on his back with hair hanging over the edge of the bed. The bed should be protected with a sheet of polythene and a towel.

Entertaining the invalid

While the patient is feeling very ill he will probably be content to spend most of the time resting and sleeping. As his condition improves he will need to be kept occupied to prevent him becoming bored. Frequently the most trying time of an illness is the early convalescence. The nurse may be finding her work tiring while the patient may be irritated at not being able to do things for himself. Consideration for each other is needed to prevent friction at this time. This applies particularly to children who usually hate being kept in bed.

You will find it necessary to provide a variety of occupations as the invalid may only be able to concentrate for a short time. Radio and television cater for nearly everyone's interests. Make sure you have a timetable of the programmes available so that viewing and listening time can be planned.

Children can make good use of a bedtable or large tray. This can serve as a base for jigsaw puzzles, building bricks, a car track or as a drawing board. Water colour painting is not a good idea but felt pens can be bought in a wide range of colours and thicknesses. Avoid very small toys which could get lost in the bed but see that other favourite toys are available. There are many card games and even a small child can be taught to play games of Patience. Older children will listen for hours to records. Books can be borrowed from a lending library but this should not be done if the illness is infectious. Crafts such as embroidery and knitting could interest a patient of either sex.

Do not leave the patient alone for long periods. Many household chores could be done sitting in a comfortable chair in the sickroom. The patient may not want you to talk or do anything for him. It is comforting just to have someone in the room. A convalescent will probably enjoy having visitors. You must see he is not overtired by their staying too long. A considerate visitor should be concerned only for the patient and not resent your tactful suggestion that the visit should be kept short.

If the patient is unable to leave the bed, you will need to hire or buy a bed pan. This should be warmed with hot water before being given to the patient. Immediately after use cover with a cloth and empty. Wash and rinse with a mild disinfectant. Once a day scald with a solution of soda.

Encourage the patient to look as attractive as possible. A man will feel better if he is shaved each day. Most women like their hair arranged attractively and to wear light cosmetics. Indeed this may be the opportunity to spend time experimenting with make up or on a manicure.

As the patient gets better he should be encouraged to gradually resume a normal routine. This should not be rushed as a relapse could occur if he overtaxes himself. Insist on plenty of rest and a sensible diet. The patient should not resume work or school before the doctor agrees to this.

The doctor

If he is to give of his best the doctor must rely on the good sense of his patients to use his services properly and economically. It is foolish to call on him for very trivial things but wise to consult him for any health matter which needs more than amateur treatment. The best rule is to seek his advice if you suddenly become ill with symptoms you do not understand or if you have gradually been feeling less well over a period of time. It would be as well to see him if you are ill for more than three days.

These rules do not apply to small children. A baby's health can deteriorate very quickly and there are times when immediate attention is necessary. Any doctor would rather be called out sooner than later to a child patient. There is no need to feel embarrassed should the child make a rapid recovery before the doctor arrives.

You will help the doctor by seeing him at his consulting rooms either during surgery hours or by appointment rather than expecting him to call on you. The time taken getting to and from your home could be used in looking after his patients.

Do not think you can treat yourself. Ignore the advice of neighbours. If you look up your symptoms in a medical book you will probably find they apply to all sorts of unlikely diseases. A book is no substitute for the doctor, he has been thoroughly trained to deal with your health problems.

If you need the doctor to call at home to see a patient you should carry out the following procedure:

1 Make sure your request for him to call reaches him before he starts on his morning rounds. This enables him to plan his work for the day and the route of his visits.

2 Give a clear message. You should give the name of the patient, his correct address and brief but clear information about the symptoms. The doctor may need to bring special equipment or medicines with him so he would like some idea of what he needs before he sets out. Do not exaggerate the seriousness of the case in order to get priority attention. Others may need his help more.

3 Be sure you are in when the doctor calls. He will need a quiet atmosphere to examine a case properly. Turn off radio or television and ask the family or visitors to go into another room.

4 It will help the doctor if you can give him as much information as possible. Tell him about temperature, pain or sickness and the condition of the patient prior to his visit. Tell the doctor about any home remedies you may have used.

5 Don't chatter while he is examining the patient. He needs to concentrate on what he is doing. If he is using a stethascope he cannot hear you anyway. Answer his questions carefully and truthfully. Neither hide nor exaggerate anything. The doctor sees the patient for a comparatively short time each visit and depends on whoever is doing the nursing to give him accurate information on the case.

6 Make sure you have hot water, soap and a clean towel available for him to wash his hands.

7 Make sure you understand the doctors instructions as to treatment. If they are complicated, or if you are forgetful write them down and ask him to check them for you. This is especially important if you are sharing the nursing.

8 The doctor may ask you to keep a record of various symptoms so that he can keep a check on progress. Do so as accurately as you can. If a variety of drugs must be given at different times you may find that a simple chart on which you indicate the time that each drug has been given will save you worry.

9 When taking medicines of any sort you should follow instructions on the pack. Remember that you are unlikely to see immediate results as most medicines need time to work. Don't be tempted to double the dose in order to halve the recovery time. Complete the course of treatment unless the doctor tells you to discontinue it. In this case dispose of the medicines in the fire or down the lavatory. Do not save them as most should be used while still fresh.

7 The Water Supply

Cholera and typhoid are just two of the ghastly diseases that are spread by contaminated water supplies. In order to ensure that the water we use is as pure as possible the Water Board is required by law to maintain an adequate supply of water free from harmful bacteria or minerals. Water in its natural state as rain, rivers and lakes is seldom pure or fit to drink. As rain falls it collects impurities from the atmosphere. It collects dust and dissolves various chemicals in the atmosphere. Near the sea it contains sodium chloride and in towns it contains sulphur dioxide and sulphuric acid from domestic fires and factories. The denser the population the greater the pollution. In the ground it is affected by the mineral content of the soil and decaying organic matter.

Rivers are continually being fouled by chemicals and sewage. People are at last becoming aware of the filthy state of many of our waterways and most local authorities are trying to improve the situation. Meanwhile many water boards find it worth their while to pipe water considerable distances to get supplies of comparatively clean water from low population areas in Scotland and Wales.

There is no shortage of rain in the British Isles. In fact the rainfall is about five times the amount we need but it does not fall in the most convenient places. Our heaviest rainfall is in the mountains and moorlands which are the lowest population areas.

The cost of installing the watermains is very high and because of this there are still a few isolated houses depending on private wells and boreholes for their water supply, but the numbers rapidly decrease as the piped water system develops.

It has been estimated that when people have to carry water from a well or a standpipe the average consumption per day is sixteen litres of water. With piped water and the use of a variety of modern bathroom and kitchen fittings the average consumption steadily rises to well over 180 litres a head. At the same time the number of people suffering from water borne diseases rapidly declines.

Remember that water is valuable and we are very fortunate in this country in being able to use it freely. Be liberal in its use but do not waste it. Do not let taps run uselessly, and see that worn tap washers are renewed promptly.

Water in the home

The water is carried from the reservoir through the town in water mains buried 60 to 90cms underground. Service pipes connect the mains to the houses. The service pipe leads to storage tanks fitted as high as possible, sometimes in the attic, so that it is above the taps and cisterns it serves. The flow of water is controlled by a ball valve. This cuts off the supply of water as soon as the tank is full. There is usually a direct supply of water to the kitchen from the service pipe, so that drinking water does not have to be taken from the tank. This is because when water was first piped to houses there was a risk of pollution in the pipes and the house storage tanks so the drinking water tap was placed at the point of entry to avoid this.

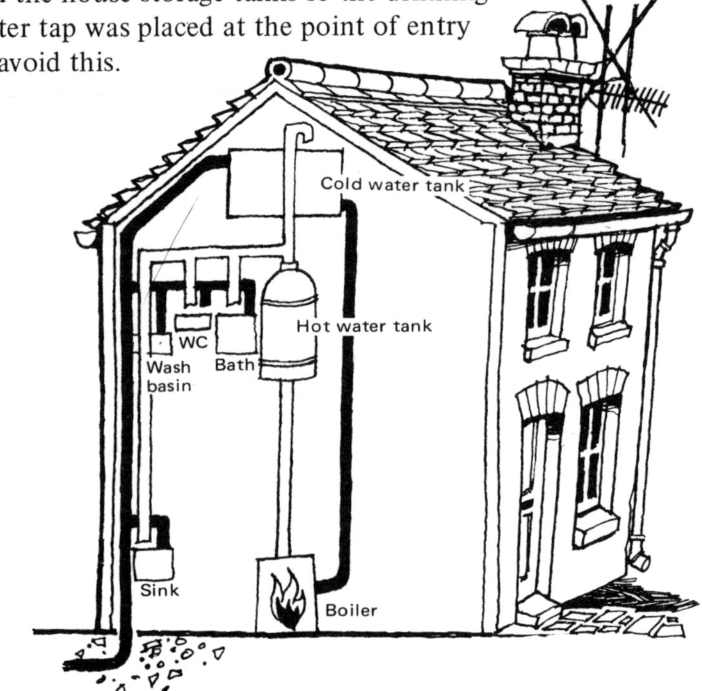

Hot water

Once the water is supplied to the house it is comparatively easy to arrange to have hot water available from the tap. Hot water not only cuts down the work of keeping a home clean but also ensures a higher standard of hygiene.

Children are more likely to enjoy washing themselves if there is plenty of hot water available than if they must wash either in cold water or ration out the hot. Doing the family washing could be sheer drudgery when the housewife had to get up early in order to light fires and boilers to get sufficient hot water. Now with the invention of easily laundered fabrics, a range of detergents and plenty of hot water clothes can be washed very easily, thus the standards of personal cleanliness have gradually improved.

Hot water is essential for
(a) Washing and bathing
(b) Dish washing
(c) Laundry
(d) Cleaning the home

The method of heating water will vary according to the needs of the household, and to the fuel used for heating and cooking. A good supply of hot water is as important in the summer as the winter so should be available even when room heating is not needed.

Whatever the source of the water it must be purified before being piped to the consumer. The public water authorities maintain constant vigil to ensure a clean safe supply of water. This may be carried out in a variety of ways but the following method is typical.

1 The water is piped from the river or lake into a storage reservoir. As the water reaches the householder by gravity the reservoir must be sited at a place higher than the highest building it supplies, otherwise pumps would be needed to get the water to the taps. This would increase costs.
2 The water is stored for a long period to allow solid parti-

cles to settle and the harmful bacteria to die. Between 96% – 99% of the bacteria are destroyed at this stage. These could include those causing typhoid, para-typhoid, dysentry and gastric enteritis.

3 The water is then filtered through a series of sand beds.

4 The water is chlorinated to kill off the remainder of the bacteria.

5 The water is constantly being tested. It may be treated with various chemicals. This vigilance is essential if the supply is to remain safe and of the same chemical composition. Many industries rely on the stability of the water supply. For example, tea is blended to suit the chemical composition of the water in each area, and the makers of detergents have to bear this in mind in deciding where each product is likely to have the highest sales.

6 The waterboards must give a constant service not only to the house-holder but to industry and various public authorities. Apart from the water you use in your own home it is used either by you or for you in numerous other places. These may include:
(a) Cleaning of streets and public places
(b) Swimming baths
(c) Public lavatories and slipper baths
(d) Hospitals
(e) Laundries
(f) Farms
(g) Industry
(h) Hotels and Restaurants

We expect a high standard of cleanliness from these places and this can only be achieved by liberal use of water.

The water rates

The householder pays for his water supplies through a water rate. The amount charged depends on the rateable value of the house, not on the amount of water used. Because this is an expensive service to run, it could be argued that it would be more businesslike to have a meter in each house to record consumption and to charge on quantity used as for gas and electricity. This system is used in many other countries. In Great Britain water is regarded as a public service which is invaluable in raising the standard of health of the nation. There is no excuse for lack of cleanliness because you cannot afford to pay for water.

Drainage

Drainage is the responsibility of the local authority. Local bye-laws give specific rules on the construction of domestic drainage. No home is given a certificate of habitation unless the local Department of Health is satisfied that the plumbing and drainage are properly constructed.

Every sanitary fitting must be made of a non absorbent material such as cast iron or plastic. They must be made with a water seal which prevents foul gases returning to the house from the drainage pipes and sewers. The water seal is made in the form of a U bend in the drainage pipe. This traps sufficient water to act as a seal.

Drainage from baths and sinks usually leads to an outside pipe. This takes the waste water to an open gulley at ground level. The waste from the lavatory is taken down a soil pipe straight to the sewer. The soil pipe has no opening at ground level. The pipe is extended up to the roof above all openings. Thus the soil pipe is ventilated without risk of gases entering the house.

Draining pipes are connected to the sewers which usually run under the road. Manholes are constructed at intervals so that the drains can be inspected. The waste is then piped to the sewage works where it is treated with chemicals and rendered harmless. The water can then be pumped out onto the land or into rivers while the treated solids may be used as fertilizer. Unfortunately not all local authorities deal so efficiently with the problem. As a result many of our rivers and beaches are being polluted by untreated sewage.

While the drainage outside the home is the responsibility of the local authority the householder must maintain the

domestic plumbing in good condition. Outside gulleys and drains can become clogged with leaves, birds nests and dirt, so regular checks are sensible. The gulleys should be cleaned regularly. Wash-day might be a suitable day to do this. Internal waste pipes may be blocked by grease and debris such as hairs, tealeaves and cloth fibres. These can quickly become a breeding ground for harmful bacteria. Try to avoid this by flushing out waste pipes with plenty of clean water after draining away any dirty water. Boiling water with soda dissolved in it will dissolve any clogging grease.
Should blockage occur it is usually a fairly simple job to clear the pipe. There are various chemical waste pipe cleaners available. A tool called a force pump or force cup is useful. Put the pump over the plug hole and push hard on the handle and then pull up sharply. Do this several times; the pump forces air down the pipe and often pushes the obstruction at the same time.

If these methods do not work you should then put a bucket under the U bend. Take out the screw at the end and remove the obstruction. Rinse out the pipe and replace the screw.

In some isolated areas it would be very expensive to connect some of the homes to main sewage system. An alternative is to have the house drains connected to a covered watertight cesspool. These must be emptied at regular intervals. The contents are pumped into mobile tanks and taken to a sewage works for treatment. If even this method of disposal is not available the problem may be solved by the use of a chemical closet. These are useful for caravans, houseboats and camping sites. Chemicals must be used exactly as instructed. The container must be emptied and cleaned regularly.

8 Hygiene in the Bathroom

Cleanliness is the best weapon against disease. It follows that every opportunity should be taken to encourage personal cleanliness. No local authority may give planning permission for a house to be built unless it has an adequate bathroom and lavatory. Local councils will give substantial grants to owners of old houses without such facilities to help them to bring their properties up to the required standards.

It is pointless having a bathroom unless it is used. It should be made as comfortable and attractive as possible, so that the most reluctant member of the family can find no excuse for not making use of it.

Decorations and colour schemes should be those favoured by the family. Bear in mind that there will be frequent changes of temperature and dampness to deal with. Wall and surface coverings must be able to take constant cleaning. Ceramic tiles, plastic or glass panels are frequently used and a number of steam resistant wallpapers are available. Woodwork should be well sealed with paint or enamel. Floors should be easy to clean, non slippery and if possible, warm to the feet. A good quality linoleum, plastic faced cork or vinyl are all suitable. Curtains of cotton seersucker, towelling or plastic will tolerate steam and not be limp on drying out. The room should be warm but well ventilated. Draughts should be avoided.

Baths and basins should be of good quality to stand up to the wear of constant use and cleaning. They may be made of porcelain or enamel, enamelled steel, fibre glass or polythene. As most bathrooms are rather small fittings are usually put next to the walls. All gaps between walls and fittings should be filled with a non porous material so that dirt and moisture cannot collect there. A shower fitted above the bath or in a separate compartment is most useful. This uses less hot water than a bath and is more hygienic as the dirt from the bather's body is washed straight down the drain. The water is ready for immediate use so saving time spent waiting for the bath to fill. It is most useful for hair washing, as soap can be thoroughly rinsed out. The minimum amount of water is used, and this can be set at a comfortable temperature.

Bathroom space is usually limited but there are various items which should be provided if the bathroom is to be a comfortable and hygienic place.

1 There should be a plentiful supply of hot water.
2 A towel rail or hook for each member of the family.
3 Towels and facecloths for each person. These should not be shared.
4 A toothbrush rack and toothbrushes for each member of the family. These should be frequently renewed.
5 A cabinet or shelves to hold toilet articles.
6 A mirror. This must be positioned in a suitable place for shaving or using cosmetics.
7 A stool or chair.
8 A container for soiled linen. This should be of a material which can be cleaned and disinfected. Plastic, compressed fire or enamelled wood are preferable to the basket variety, as these tend to catch on threads of fine fabrics and are difficult to keep really clean.
9 Storage for cleaning materials.
10 A wastepaper bin for cartons and wrappings.
11 The bathroom heating could be incorporated into a radiator or towel rail so that damp towels could be dried off after use.

It is preferable that the W.C. should be a separate room from the bathroom. This is not always possible in a small house. If the lavatory and bathroom are combined it is sometimes possible to have a second lavatory on the ground floor. This is particularly useful when there are young children or old people who have difficulty climbing the stairs.

It is essential that all surfaces can be washed and disinfected frequently. Similar floor and wall coverings to those chosen for the bathroom are generally used. Fittings should be chosen with cleanliness as the first consideration.

The W.C. pan and seat should be of simple design with as few crevices and crannies as possible. These are difficult to keep clean and are ideal places for bacteria to breed. A foot operated pedal on the cistern eliminates the use of hands in working the flush. Choose good quality absorbent lavatory paper and a neat holder.

There should be an efficient ventilator which should not be closed even in cold weather. There are a number of aids available to keep the air smelling fresh. Aerosols can be used or slow dissolving blocks of solid disinfectants which can be hung in the W.C. pan or the cistern.

Decorative mats and seat covers should be avoided. Unless they can be changed very frequently they are liable to become a breeding ground for bacteria.

Ideally every lavatory should have a handbasin with a supply of hot water and soap. Hands should be washed immediately after using the W.C. Children should be trained to do this from the very earliest age. Many infectious diseases are spread by neglecting to do this.

All surfaces in the lavatory must be properly cleaned at frequent intervals. The seat and all handles must be wiped over daily with a disinfectant solution. Household bleach is suitable for the purpose. The floor and walls must be washed regularly. The W.C. pan should be thoroughly cleaned at least once a week. There are many proprietary cleaners on the market. Follow instructions carefully and do not mix any two chemicals. If a lavatory brush is used it should be disinfected after use and hung outside to dry.

Remember that most lavatory cleaners must be used very carefully and should not be left within reach of small children. If they are to be stored in the lavatory they should be in a locked cupboard out of reach of children. A spare packet of lavatory paper could also be kept here.

9 Hygiene in the Kitchen

The kitchen is the base for the storage, preparation, cooking and serving of food. It should therefore be planned with food hygiene as the most important factor.

1 A good supply of hot water is essential.
2 All surfaces should be smooth and easily cleaned, they should be dirt and grease resistant.
3 Avoid ledges and corners where dust and grease can collect.
4 Joins and cracks in work surfaces are difficult to keep clean even if you can move the units. Continuous work tops are neater and more hygienic than individual ones. Laminated plastics can now be bought in lengths and widths sufficient for most needs. Bridged cavities can be left for washing machines and refrigerators which cannot be built in.
5 Floor covering must be of good quality. It needs to be unaffected by spilled grease and food, and by the frequent washing needed to keep it really clean.

6 Walls should be covered with an easily cleaned surface. Tiles, plastics, gloss paint and washable wallpapers can be bought in a wide range of colours and textures so that the kitchen can be attractive as well as hygienic.

7 Ceiling finishes should be resistant to condensation and grease. Enamel and plastic emulsion paints are both easy to apply and to clean when necessary.

8 Good lighting is essential. Full use should be made of natural light. This must be supplimented by artificial lighting so that every section of the kitchen is well illuminated including the cupboards.

9 Ventilation needs special attention. Condensation and food smells can both be a problem. These can be controlled by sufficient window openings and air vents, air conditioners and cooker hoods. Stale air may not only make the kitchen stuffy but may also be laden with dust and germs.

Food Hygiene

The number of widespread outbreaks of food poisoning have dropped appreciably in the last twenty years. The number of domestic outbreaks has hardly changed in this time. It seems obvious from this that local authorities, food distributors, caterers and others concerned with mass feeding have all worked to improve the standards of food hygiene. Unfortunately the standards in the home have not equalled this improvement.

We tend to ignore what we cannot see. Many food poisoning organisms cannot be seen. Food spoiled by bacteria may taste, smell and look normal. Food poisoning is not a new problem. It has been recognised since the very earliest time. Many of the taboos and rules concerning food upheld by our earliest ancestors originated in practical knowledge of the problem.

It was not until the 17th century that bacteria were first seen through a microscope by Van Leeuwenhock. He was a draper whose hobby was making microscopes and he examined everything he could think of. The significance of his discovery was only realised two hundred years later by Louis Pasteur. His work opened up a completely new field of study in relation to bacteria and disease.

We cannot all be trained biologists, but we can make use of their discoveries to help keep us free from harmful organisms.

Bacteria, Yeasts, and Moulds

These are simple plant forms too small to be seen by the naked eye. Given suitable conditions of warmth, moisture, oxygen and food they will multiply rapidly. Growth can be slowed down by depriving the plant of one or more of these favourable conditions. This is the basis of all the care needed to ensure that food is safe to eat. Not all these microorganisms are harmful. Indeed we make use of some in cheese and breadmaking and in fermenting wines and beer. On the other hand some are harmful and can be dangerous if allowed to multiply.

Bacteria causing food poisoning

1 Salmonellae

These organisms live naturally in the soil and in the bowels of humans and other animals. They are seldom harmful in the small numbers normally present. It is when they are allowed to contaminate food that they multiply rapidly and become a danger. It is therefore vital to stress the importance of washing the hands after a visit to the lavatory as this can easily become a source of infection. Animals must be kept out of the kitchen and away from any human food. They should have their own food dishes.

Salmonella poisoning is very serious. It can prove fatal particularly to the very young, the elderly or people already ill. Illness usually occurs about twelve to thirtysix hours after eating the infected food. The patient will have a high temperature, abdominal pain, diarrhoea and sickness. Infection may last up to a week.

The organism breeds particularly rapidly on meat and poultry. All meats should be cooked thoroughly. If required cold they should be cooled rapidly. Cooked and uncooked meats should not be stored together as the cooked meat could easily be contaminated by bacteria in the uncooked meat.

Duck eggs may be a useful addition to the family's diet, but they need to be cooked thoroughly if infection is to be avoided. A duck egg must be boiled for at least 15 minutes to be safe, or fried thoroughly on both sides. They must never be preserved or eaten uncooked or used in dishes which are only lightly cooked.

2 Staphylococci

More than fifty per cent of normal people carry staphylococci bacteria in the nose and throat. About a quarter of these carry the bacteria in their hands. Our hands will almost certainly become contaminated when we touch our nose or mouth on using a handkerchief. Boils, ulcers and septic cuts are caused by staphylococci and are likely to be heavily infected by these organisms. In suitable conditions the bacteria reproduce themselves every twenty minutes developing toxins as they do so. Washing hands before handling food will help to prevent the spread of infection. A good supply of paper handkerchiefs which can be disposed of immediately after use is preferable to those of linen which harbour the bacteria. All cuts and lesions should be covered by a waterproof dressing.

The incubation of the poison may be as short as two hours but is usually 4 – 6 hours. There is usually severe pain, vomiting and diarrhoea followed sometimes by collapse. Recovery is usually rapid.

3 Clostridium Welchii

The organisms of this group grow only in the absence of air. The spores themselves are harmless. They survive almost indefinitely in soil and dust and in the air. It is only in the suitable conditions of warmth and lack of air such as in the middle of a joint or a slow cooking stew that they will multiply to danger level. Ninety per cent of this type of food poisoning is traced to meat and meat products. Food should be cooked right through to more than 50°C. If it is to be served cold, cooling should be rapid down to below 15°C. The dangerous temperature zone is that between 15°C and 50°C.

The symptoms of poisoning are usually mild and usually last for about 24 hours.

Internal Parasites
Food may also be infected by living organisms. There are a number of intestinal worms parasitic to man. Fortunately of these, only the common roundworm, threadworms and tapeworms are likely to be seen in this country. The eggs of the roundworm and threadworm may be taken in with contaminated food or water. The eggs develop in the human body and adult worms live in the intestines where the female will lay many eggs. They pass from the body in faeces. Medical treatment is needed but the cycle can only be broken if the hands are kept clean and by frequent changes of personal linen and towels.

Tapeworms
The beef and pork tapeworms live in the human intestine but have their embryo stage in the animal. The infection by both types of worm can be prevented by making sure all beef and pork meat, and meat products are thoroughly cooked.

Dog tapeworm
This worm lives in the intestine of dogs. The eggs may be passed to man in infected food. Prevention consists of careful handwashing after handling dogs and before meals. Dogs should be kept out of the kitchen or wherever food is stored or prepared.

The Handling of Food

Food should be handled as little as possible. To ensure safety all the following rules must be followed.

1 Hands should always be washed with hot water and soap before handling food and after each occasion when they may have become recontaminated.

2 Long hair should be tied back and clean aprons worn.

3 Care must be taken not to sneeze or cough over food. If possible a person with a cold should stay out of the kitchen.

4 Use paper handkerchiefs in the kitchen. Dispose of them hygienically after use and then wash hands.

5 All cuts and sores on hands and arms should be covered with waterproof dressings.

6 Attacks of vomiting or diarrhoea may be a symptom of food poisoning or other infectious illness. Anyone so affected should not handle food as the infection could spread rapidly.

Food Storage

No food in its natural form will stay in perfect condition indefinitely no matter how it is stored. Micro-organisms will bring about a change in composition. Most of the organisms which affect food will spoil it. This causes wastage. Some organisms will cause food poisoning and serious illness.

The facilities for storing food will vary according to the size of the kitchen and the money available for equipment. Whatever the storage it should be dry, cool and perfectly clean. This is obvious when you remember that micro-organisms thrive in moist, warm and dirty conditions.

A cool larder is ideal but in most cases the food store is a kitchen cupboard. Shelves of the food cupboard should be of an easily cleaned material where no dirt can lodge. Marble is ideal but expensive. Plastic laminates are very efficient. The initial cost may be high but no further expense is involved. Less permanent but good sealed surfaces can be made with thin adhesive plastic film, paint or liquid plastic.

The floor and walls of the cupboard should be easily cleaned.

If it is ventilated by a window this should be covered by flyproof metal gauze.

Food containers should have tightly fitted lids so as to be damp and insect proof. If the food is left in the paper packets in which it is bought these may become damp and contaminated by insects.

Food which deteriorates quickly or loses flavour if stored should be bought in small quantities as needed. Fresh fruit and vegetables should not be stored but bought as needed and used as soon as possible. The vitamin value of these diminishes rapidly.

Tinned and bottled foods, ultra heat treated milk and cream, and various dried food may be stored for a fairly long time as long as they are kept dry and cool.

Many fresh foods will deteriorate very rapidly unless stored at a very low temperature such as in a refrigerator or deep freeze. These include meat, fish and milk.

The housewife should keep a regular check on her food stores. Food should be used while still fresh. This will not only prevent wastage but will ensure that the family is only given safe food to eat. Economy is important but when in any doubt as to the safety of the food it is better to throw it out rather than risk the family health. Food which is not to be consumed immediately should be cooked through and then cooled rapidly. It should not be left in a warm oven or a warm kitchen. When cooled it should be stored in a refrigerator. Where reheating is necessary it is essential that boiling point should be reached in every part of the food.

Where possible a refrigerator should be used to store fresh perishable food. At temperature below 10°C bacterial activity is greatly reduced so that food stays in good condition for 3 to 4 days. It is a mistake to think that because we have a temperate climate refrigerators are not needed. The kitchen is often warmer in the winter than in the summer and as windows are less likely to be opened there is also the problem of moisture.

The use of a refrigerator allows for a wider choice of foods and virtually no need for wastage. The housewife should include the refrigerator in her daily check on the food store. Even at this low temperature growth of organisms is not stopped, merely slowed down.

Avoid putting hot food into the refrigerator as this will raise the temperature inside. The refrigerator must be cleaned and defrosted regularly according to maker's instructions. Improvised cooling methods are valuable when a refrigerator is not obtainable. Porous earthenware covers cooled with water keep butter, milk and other foods cool by evaporation. Stand milk bottles and other food containers in a bowl of water. Cover container with muslin allowing edge of this to fall down into the water. Insulated containers can be made from sheets of polystyrene. Remember that a vacuum flask keeps foods cold equally as well as it keeps them hot.
While a refrigerator will only protect food for a few days a deep freeze has a temperature of below 18°C and will preserve certain foods for months. Food destroying bacteria will not multiply at such low temperature.

Washing up

This is sometimes regarded as the most menial and boring of all household chores. Because of this its real importance is overlooked and there is little enthusiasm in doing the job properly. It is worth while tackling the work in a methodical way. Not only will this simplify the task but give a far better standard of cleanliness than if carried out in a slap-dash way.

The work entails five processes –
Preparation, washing, rinsing, drying and draining – in that order. Before you start make sure you have the equipment necessary to carry out each operation.

Ideally there should be a work top next to the sinks for stacking the dirty dishes, a double sink, a draining board and another work top to stack the clean dry dishes. Unfortunately this arrangement takes up a lot of space and it is usually necessary to improvise to achieve the same effect. Plastic bowls are inexpensive and a draining rack on a plastic tray can be substituted for a draining board.

The most essential requirement is a constant supply of really hot water. It should be as hot as the hand can bear for washing and at a higher temperature than this for rinsing. If water of a lower temperature has to be used a suitable disinfectant is recommended.

There are a number of powders and liquid detergents available for washing up. Some people find these affect the hands but it is generally when too much is used. Use according to instructions on bottle or packet. If the hands are especially sensitive or if there is an unusual amount of washing up to be done it is sensible to use rubber gloves. A dish mop with plastic handle and nylon bristles is preferable to a dish cloth.

1 Preparation

(a) Scrape food off plates and dishes. Put those with baked-on food to soak in warm water.

(b) Rinse empty cups, teapots, jugs and glasses. If they have contained milk this should be rinsed out with cold water.

(c) Stack dishes neatly ready for washing up in the following order – glass, cutlery, crockery and finally pans and cooking utensils.

2 Rinsing and draining

Each article should be washed, rinsed straight away and then put into a draining rack. If the water is really hot most of the dishes will be dry within a few minutes.

Both washing and rinsing water should be changed if it becomes dirty or cools down. Lukewarm dirty water will encourage survival and multiplication of bacteria.

3 Drying

If the rinsing water is really hot the dishes will probably need only a final polish before being put away. Disposable paper towels cut down the possibility of bacteria being transferred to the clean dishes. If it is necessary to use cloths they must be washed and boiled frequently or washed out and treated with hypochloride.

4 The clean dishes should be put away so that they are not exposed to contamination by dust and flies.

5 The sink, bowl and draining boards should be washed and dried. Cloths should be washed out and put to dry, if possible in the open air.

Dishwashing machines

Apart from the obvious one of saving time and labour there are many advantages in washing dishes in a machine.

1 The water used in the machine can be far hotter than hands could bear.

2 Powerful detergents may be used which would be too strong for the skin.

3 The dishes are thoroughly washed rinsed and dried at very high temperatures thus destroying most of the harmful bacteria.

4 No teacloth is needed.

5 The machine is self cleaning on the inside.

6 In most homes the machine need only be used once a day. After each meal the dishes should be scraped of food and stacked in special racks in the machine. The kitchen remains tidy and there are no dirty dishes left out to attract flies and other pests.

Disinfectants

We tend to think of disinfectants as proprietary liquids bought from the chemist or ironmonger. This is but one type of disinfectant. Disinfectation is a process which kills bacteria. In the home this can be done in several ways.

1 Using sunlight – the ultra violet rays kill bacteria.

2 Using heat. Fire is the best purifier of all. Infected articles which will not be needed again may be burnt but such drastic action is not always necessary if the article can be

boiled. Boiling will kill all germs and it is a useful method of disinfecting towels, crockery and bed linen. The articles must be boiled for at least one hour to be really effective.

3 Using bleaching powders and liquids.

4 Using liquid germicides such as carbolic.

Antiseptics are not really disinfectants. They do not kill the germs but merely retard their growth and development.

Take care when using any of the chemical disinfectants as some of them are poisonous. Follow instructions for use exactly in order to get the best results. Lock them up out of reach of children. Never put them into a food container such as a milk or lemonade bottle.

A clean, well ventilated home plays an important part in keeping the family healthy, but sometimes stricter precautions are necessary.

If it is necessary for a house or room to be disinfected after a serious infectious illness, the local council will usually arrange to have this done. They will also take away and treat articles not easy to deal with at home such as mattresses, pillows and blankets. Remember that it is illegal to send infected articles to a public laundry. A severe fine can be incurred. They must be disinfected first. If you have any queries about this the Public Health Department of your local council will give you advice and help.

Laundry

The kitchen is not the ideal place to do the laundry. Dirty clothes near food are unhygienic. Most of these dirty clothes are discarded in bedrooms and bathrooms. It is often possible to re-arrange even a small bathroom to double as a laundry room. If you have a fully automatic washing machine the place where you keep it is governed only by the plumbing. It could be in the garage, conservatory or a lobby.

If the kitchen is the only possibility it is sensible to take the following precautions to avoid the contamination of food by bacteria.

1 Sort out the clothes in a different room preferably the bathroom.
2 Open kitchen ventilators to allow steam to escape from the kitchen.
3 Do the washing as quickly as possible.
4 Wipe down all contaminated surfaces with a disinfectant solution.
5 Do not boil clothes or handkerchiefs in cooking utensils. Keep separate equipment for laundry use only.

10 Refuse Disposal

There are numerous bins designed for kitchen use. Make sure you choose one of suitable size. It should be emptied daily and kept clean and dry. A foot operated opening device cuts down the need for touching with the hands. The most hygienic models to use are those incorporating replaceable paper or plastic bags. There are several types available which heat seal the filled bags with an electrical device. This helps keep the main dustbin fly and vermin-free.

Sink waste disposal units

These are small machines fitted under the sink and connected to the waste pipe. The sink outlet to the pipe is enlarged so that the waste can be put through it. The machine is powered by electricity.

It deals effectively with food waste, bones and glass which are all ground down to a fine pulp which can then be washed away. It cannot take string, tin, cloth or plastics. The tap should be left running while the machine is operating and for a while afterwards to make sure it is cleaned through.

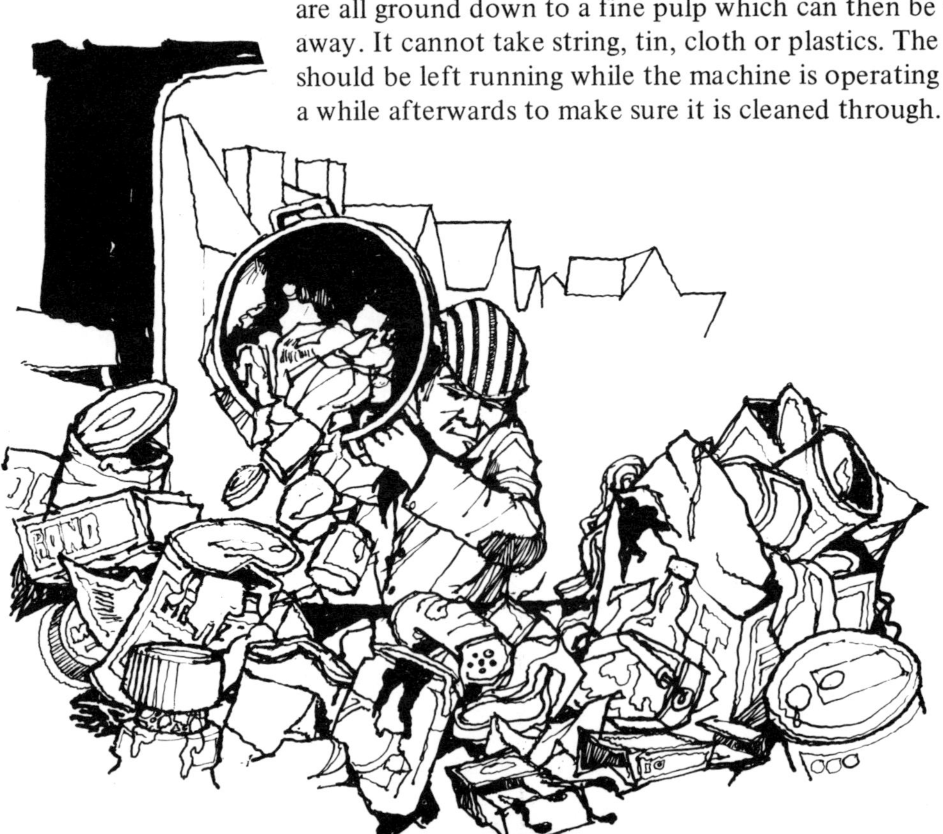

In the past one of the drawbacks about having such a machine fitted was that should the unit be out of order the sink above could not be used. It is now possible to buy a model which can be disconnected from the waste pipe and replaced with a special piece of piping. Manufacturers do not recommend you to try to clean any blockage yourself. Young children should not be allowed to use the machine as they may put their hand down into the grinding blades. The batch food type is the safest in that it will only work with a lid in place over grinding blades. Should there be a blockage the electricity should be switched off even when the emergency cut-out has stopped the machine working.

These machines are particularly useful where it is difficult to cope with kitchen waste such as large blocks of flats. There is one drawback which will have to be faced by the local authorities as the use of these units becomes widespread. Some method will have to be found to prevent an increase in the sewer rat population, which will obviously benefit from the extra food supply.

Refuse Disposal

Most local authorities do arrange for all household rubbish to be collected at regular intervals. It can still be a problem to know how to deal with it in a hygienic way while awaiting collection. The volume of refuse increases every year. More goods are bought packaged and wrapped and more disposable articles are being used. In the past much of this would have been burnt by the householder. Now fewer homes have the facilities for doing this. Those in smokeless zones would probably be breaking the law should they do so.

The most convenient way to store the rubbish is in a dustbin. In some areas these are actually provided by the local authorities. The bins may be made of a variety of materials including galvanised metal, plastic and paper. All should fulfil the following conditions.

1 They should have well fitted lids to prevent access by flies and rodents.

2 Bins should be kept as clean as possible. The paper sack variety is the most hygienic as the sack is disposed of with the rubbish and replaced by a new one.
3 All other types should be washed out and disinfected regularly.
4 All food waste and wet garbage should be well wrapped up in paper, or in plastic bags, before being put into the bin. Rinse out food cans.
5 Outside bins should be kept as far from the kitchen as possible. Choose a well ventilated place out of the sunlight. Rust at the base of metal bins can be avoided by standing the bin on bricks so that air can circulate under the base and keep it dry.
6 Many local councils salvage certain refuse such as metals and paper. Should this be so in your area, you should keep these materials separate from the other rubbish. The council sells the salvage and this helps to keep down the local rates.
7 Make sure the bin is accessible to the dustmen for collection. If you have to carry it any distance arrange for help or have a simple trolley made. Do not carry a very heavy bin by yourself.

The ordinary dustcart can only cope with small household refuse. You may need to dispose of bulky items such as mattresses or armchairs. The local council can arrange for collection and disposal of these, usually without charge. Old cars may also be collected by some councils but a small charge is usually made for this service. Remember that the Litter Act of 1958 forbids the depositing of rubbish in public places. It is difficult to understand why people leave themselves open to prosecution when councils provide these services.

11 Pest Control

Ants There are about thirty different species of ants in this country. It is the black garden ant which is most likely to invade the home. The ant nest is a socially well organised community. If a group of worker ants foraging for food should be exterminated it will be replaced quickly by another group. Therefore the only way to completely rid your home of these visitors is to destroy the nest.

The ants usually come into the house for food. They are attracted by the smell of sugar. They like all sugary foods such as jam, cakes and sweets, so these must be stored carefully.

In the garden they feed on insects and seeds. The nest is usually to be found in the flower beds, under the garden path or in dead tree stumps.

Many proprietary ant destroyers are available. These can be bought in the form of powder, sprays and emulsions. Care must be taken that they do not come in contact with food or domestic pets. The insecticide should be used at two week intervals, paying special attention to skirting boards, and spaces around sinks, stores, boilers etc.

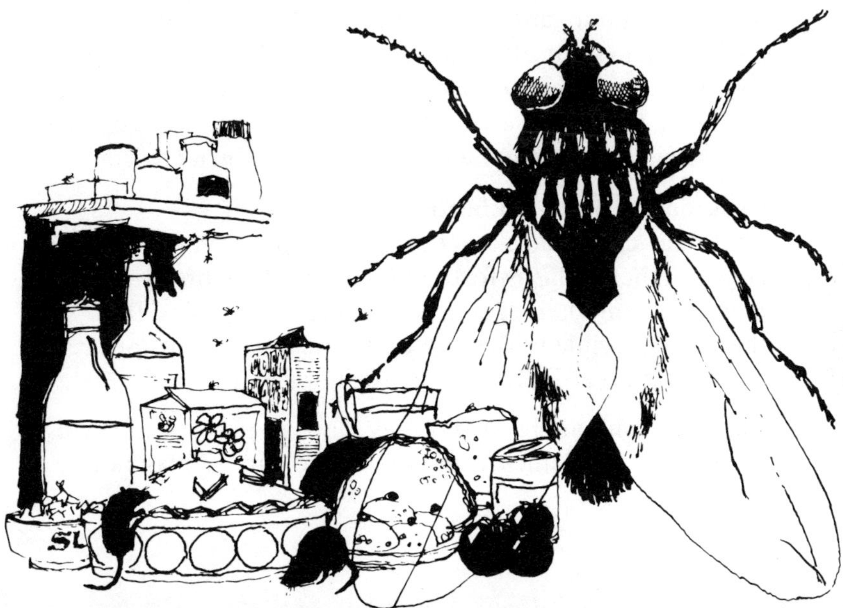

Insecticidal paints can be used around cracks in floors or walls and on window and door sills around air vents.

A really bad infestation may need to be treated by an expert using sodium fluoride poison. The local Public Health Inspector will give advice when necessary.

Bed bugs
These are small oval insects about five millimetres long. They live on blood, preferably human. To get it they puncture the skin of the host causing intense irritation. They can live for about six months without food, and usually only come out at night, so are extremely difficult to exterminate.

Fortunately they are on the decline and are usually only found in very old buildings. They breed very rapidly, living in crevices in walls, furniture and bedding and behind wallpaper. Cleanliness is the best safeguard. Spraying with insecticides and scrubbing with carbolic soap will usually deal with minor infestation. For more serious cases you should consult the local Medical Officer of Health. He can arrange for the disinfestation of bedding and clothing although he may recommend that these should be burnt.

Bees
These only become a problem should a swarm of bees decide to settle in your garden or on the house. Do not attempt to remove them yourself. Many local councils make arrangements with members of the Beekeepers Association to help by taking the swarm away. The names and addresses of these beekeepers are usually kept at the local Council Offices.

Cockroaches and blackbeetles

Cockroaches and blackbeetles seldom appear in the home in large numbers. This is fortunate because they breed very rapidly, laying their eggs in warm accessible places. It is therefore sensible to destroy them as soon as they appear, as an infestation is difficult to control or clear.

They contaminate food and they leave an unpleasant smell. They move very quickly and prefer the dark so may not be detected easily.

The places where they are most likely to be found are warm and dark. Insecticides containing DDT and pyrethrum should be sprayed around fireplaces, behind radiators, under cooking stoves and between skirting boards and floors. This should be done at night, the time of most activity. Insecticide lacquer may be painted on wood work and walls.

Earwigs

Cut down any plants growing up under windows and paint sills with insecticidal paints. This will discourage entry to the house. If they are already in the house insecticidal powders and sprays will usually kill them.

Paradichlorbenzine crystals are also useful and these will discourage moths at the same time.

Mosquitoes

If you get an excessive number of these it would be as well to find the breeding area. This may be a stagnant pond nearby which should be sprayed with DDT. Float a tablespoon of paraffin on the water in the rainwater butt.

Flies

The fly is a menace to health. There are several types to be found in houses during the summer. The most dangerous is the common housefly. Food poisoning, typhoid, dysentry, diarrhoea, the eggs of the parasitic worm and possibly poliomyelitis can all be spread by flies.

The fly carries disease in several ways:

1 It feeds on any refuse from manure to decayed vegetable matter. While doing so the feet become contaminated.

2 The decayed food which may contain various disease organisms passes through the fly and is excreted wherever it may rest. Its contaminated feet may land on food.

3 When feeding it brings up its previous meal on to its present one. This helps digestion. It then absorbs both meals.

4 It will lay eggs in food as well as refuse. It can lay up to 900 eggs in a lifetime of about five weeks. These eggs mature in about 10 days.

Flies must be prevented from breeding by entering the home and alighting on food. All refuse containers should be kept covered with tightly fitted lids. Food refuse should be wrapped in paper before being put into the bin. Kitchen bins should be emptied as soon as they are full and be cleaned daily. Dirty dishes and utensils should be washed as soon as possible and put away in a closed cupboard. Keep kitchen work surfaces and floors clean. All food should be kept covered and stored in a flyproof larder or a refrigerator. A meat safe is useful. Flyscreens should be fitted to windows and ventilators, particularly in the larder. Plastic strip screens fitted to the kitchen door discourage flying insects from entering.

Flies must be killed using every means available.

1 Aerosol sprays containing pyrethrum, DDT or Gammexane.
2 Fly strips which kill either by trapping the flies or by giving off poisonous vapours.
3 Fly swatters.
4 Insecticidal paints for ceiling and walls.
5 By destroying or spraying every possible breeding place.

Fleas

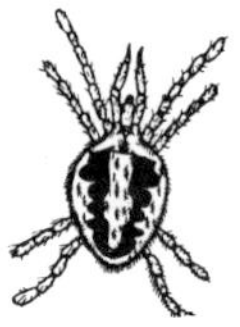

Fleas are brown wingless insects with very strong back legs for jumping. They live on blood and will die in a few days if deprived of this, otherwise they can live for months. Their bite is very irritating and scratching to relieve this may introduce infection. Eggs are laid in dust, bedding or cracks in woodwork. It takes about six weeks for the egg to develop to maturity, therefore fleas are unlikely to develop in great numbers in a home that is regularly cleaned and the dirt removed. If fleas are already well established you should first get rid of all dust and dirt on old carpets and bedding which can harbour them. Wash curtains loose covers and bedclothes, then scrub the room and furniture with soap and water concentrating on cracks and crevices. Open windows and when the room has dried out blow or brush DDT powder into all cracks in floor and furniture, and into bedding and curtains. In cases of serious infestation it is sensible to get the help of the local Public Health Department.

Lice

These are no longer a serious problem because the incidence of infection has been reduced by improved housing conditions and higher standards of hygiene. Health visitors and school nurses have played an important part in helping reduce the incidence of infection in children by the regular checks given by the school nurse and these should not be resented. It is by the systematic examination of every child that the problem has been efficiently controlled.

While there are three varieties of lice which attack man the only one you are likely to have to deal with is the head louse. This is a tiny light grey insect that lives on the scalp. It lives on blood and the bite is intensely irritating. The eggs, called nits, are white and are laid close to the scalp usually behind the ears. Each is in a little case which is stuck to the hair with a cement-like secretion from the louse. The louse lays sixty or more eggs in a month. These hatch out within a week and are fully grown in two or three weeks.

The treatment must be carried out carefully over at least ten days. The hair and scalp must be treated with an emulsion of DDT and pyrethrins obtainable from the chemist. After twentyfour hours the hair should be washed and the hair must then be combed every day, for at least ten days, with a fine toothcomb. The effect of the DDT will persist during this time and kill the nits as they hatch out.

While brushes, combs and hats should never be shared, this s fact should be stressed even more plainly should one member of the family be infected. The lice will spread to the others unless great care is taken. Brushes, combs and bed linen should be regularly disinfected to prevent the problem spreading. Most educational authorities would prefer an infected child to stay away from school while the infestation is being dealt with.

Mice and rats

Because of the improving standards of hygiene and garbage disposal in this country the rodent population has been kept in check. It would be foolish to become complacent because of this. Rats are a world wide problem. It has been found that any ready source of food such as piles of untended garbage quickly leads to a rapid increase in the rat population. Rats breed at an alarming rate. In theory, given ideal living conditions a pair of rats could produce twenty million descendants within three years.

The rat is riddled with disease and infected by parasites. These may be passed on to humans in contaminated foods, by being bitten by the fleas which live on rats or directly by rat bites. The most frightening disease connected with rats is the Plague. A more common complaint is fever and weakness caused by eating undercooked pork contaminated with parasitic threadworm. The brown rat is the main factor in the spread of these. The threadworm embryo continues to develop in the human intestine and later in the tissues and muscles.

Mice are to be found everywhere in Great Britain. Each colony restricts itself to a small area. They do a great deal of damage by gnawing cables, fabrics and wood. They foul food and water causing salmonellosis, typhoid and dysentery.

Rodents usually enter the house through holes in the floor and are invariably searching for food. Discourage them by seeing that all food is carefully stored. All spilt food and edible refuse should be cleared and put into a dustbin with a tightly fitted lid. Fill in all entry holes. Replace broken air bricks and cover them with a fine mesh wire net. A mouse can get through a gap as small as a centimetre wide.

If you keep chickens or rabbits make sure the food is kept in a rodent proof container and that chicken houses and hutches are cleaned out regularly. Compost heaps in the garden should be properly made up and well covered with soil. In most areas the garbage is regularly collected by the local authority. If for some reason this is not done it would be sensible to burn the rubbish rather than allowing an excess to accumulate.

It is comparatively easy to rid the premises of rats and mice. Owning a cat is a good way of dealing with mice while a dog of the terrier type will usually cope with the rat problem. Traps may be used but they must be baited properly and set in the runs. Wear gloves when handling the traps as rodents fear the smell of humans. Bait with bread or oatmeal which is more tempting than cheese.

Virus poisons may be used. One of the poisons used extensively contains Warfarin but in some areas the rodents have built up a resistance to this.

Do not expect immediate results from these poisons. Check bait daily and replenish as necessary until feeding stops completely. Follow the manufacturer's instructions exactly taking special care if there are children or pets in the house. The rodents die painlessly. Should you find any dead bodies they should be burnt. If a domestic pet catches a virus-poisoned rat or mouse it will not be harmed as it would if you used other poisons.

If you cannot clear the infestation yourself, or if the problem re-occurs in spite of taking precautions, you should notify your local council. A rodent officer will help you to get rid of the pests and give you any advice you may need to prevent re-occurence. No charge is made. In any case most local authorities would like to be told of any outbreaks so that a check is kept on the situation and to prevent a spread of the problem. There are commercial firms who do this work but they are usually called in for industrial premises.

Wasps

A good aerosol fly killer will destroy the occasional wasp which enters your home. Be careful not to touch the bodies of the wasps just after they have been knocked down as they may still be able to sting. If you see more than just a few wasps then it is more than likely there is a nest nearby. This should be located and destroyed. If it is in an inaccessible place call in the local sanitary inspector.

Some of the Voluntary Services and other Associations who give help and advice.

The British Red Cross Society.
The National Council for Social Services.
The Central Council for the Disabled.
The National Old Peoples Welfare Council.
The National Corporation for the care of Old People.
The Royal Society for the Prevention of Accidents.
The Fire Protection Association.
The British Standards Institute.
The British Electrical Approval Board.
The Oil Manufacturers Association.

Health Services

National Health Service
General Medical and Dental Services
Pharmaceutical Services
Opthalmic Services
Hospital Services

Regional Health Services
Blood Transfusion
Mass Radiography

Environmental Health Services
(given by Local Authority)
Housing Inspection
Food Inspection
Nuisance Control
Water Supplies
Control of Infectious Diseases
Sanitation and Sewage
Public Cleaning and Refuse Disposal
Rodent Control

Personal Health Services
(administered by Local Authority)
Maternity and Child Welfare
School Medical Services
Family Planning Clinics
Midwifery Services
Immunisation and vaccination
Home Helps
Home Nursing
Ambulance Service
Health Centres
Health Visiting
Services for the elderly in their own homes
Welfare services for the blind, the deaf, and the handicapped
Residential accommodation for the elderly or handicapped, temporary and permanent